JENNI

ABOUNL   .

A comedy with music

Book and Lyrics by
ANTHONY BUCKERIDGE

Music by
HECTOR CORTES and WILLIAM GOMEZ

Additional Music and Arrangement by
NIGEL CARVER

SAMUEL   FRENCH

LONDON
NEW YORK   TORONTO   SYDNEY   HOLLYWOOD

Please note our NEW ADDRESS:

Samuel French Ltd
52 Fitzroy Street London W1P 6JR
Tel: 01 - 387 9373

CHARACTERS

John Jennings
Emma Walker
Christine Archer
Alan Temple
Charles Darbishire
Mr Wilkins
Graham Venables
Rowena Binns
Mr Carter
Headmaster
Matron
Irving Borrowmore
Boys and Girls as extras

The action takes place at Linbury Court, a co-educational boarding school, at the end of term

ACT I   Evening
ACT II
   Scene 1   Two days later. Afternoon
   Scene 2   The next day. Evening

Time—the present

Jennings Abounding! was produced at New College School, Oxford, on July 7th, 1978 and at the Little Theatre, Lewes on December 28th, 1978, with the following cast:

John Jennings	Danny Marshall
Alan Temple	James Newton-Price
Christine Archer	Miranda Metyear
Emma Walker	Claire Hodgson
Charles Darbishire	Nicholas Cory-Wright
Mr Wilkins	Anthony Buckeridge
Graham Venables	Matthew Tapp
Rowena Binns	Polly Thomas
Mr Carter	Tony Potter
Headmaster	Kenneth Bloomfield
Matron	Ann Thomas
Irving Borrowmore	Jack Partlett
Form 3	Paul Jackson
	Tara Lamont
	Belinda Sykes
	Sally Fryer
	Matthew Kettle
	Peter Arlett
	Adam Jacobs

Musical Director	Alan Skull
Oboe	Andrew King
Flute	Anne Hodgson
Saxophone	Philippa Caddy
String Bass	Mike Bell
Percussion	Mike Preston
Piano	Corin Buckeridge

Choreography	Stella Stone
Set Design	Colin Fuller
Directed by	Eileen Buckeridge

MUSIC CUES

ACT I

1. Overture
2. Song   SCHOOL SONG   Recorded. Orchestra tacet
3. Crossover   Children crossing stage
4. Song   FAMOUS FIRST WORDS   Darbishire
4a. Reprise   FAMOUS FIRST WORDS   Darbishire (attaca No 5)
5. Song   EARTHMAN, GO HOME   Emma, Chris and girls
6. Song   THREE BOOS FOR SIR   Jennings, Emma, Chris, Darbishire and others
7. Song   THE THINGS THEY DO   Mr Wilkins, Matron, Mr Carter
8. Crossover for children crossing stage at dormitory bell
9. Reprise   THE THINGS THEY DO   Mr Wilkins
10. Song   RHUBARB   Jennings, Darbishire, Temple, Venables
11. Song   FIRE DRILL   All children (except Jennings) All staff
11a. Exit   FIRE DRILL   For children's exit
11b. Reprise   FIRE DRILL   All children and staff
12. Entr'acte

ACT II

SCENE 1

13. Song   CROSSING OFF THE DAYS   All children
13a. Exit and Melos   CROSSING OFF THE DAYS   All children for exit
14. Song   I CAN SEE MYSELF   Mr Wilkins
15. Song   UNMUSICAL MOB   Rowena
16. Music backing for children setting desks after bell for school
17. Reprise   THREE BOOS FOR SIR   Children of Form 3
18. Scene change, leading to No. 19

SCENE 2

19. Backing for dialogue
    I CAN SEE MYSELF
20. Song   I NEVER KNEW   Darbi, Emma, Chris,
                MATRONS HAD   Jen, Rowena and others
                BIRTHDAYS
20a. Melos   Children crossing stage
21. Reprise   UNMUSICAL MOB   Rowena
22. Song   NO ROOM IN THE   Irving Borrowmore
                PROFESSION
23. Duet   IT'S NOT EASY TO   Matron, Mr Carter
                FORGET
24. Song   SCHOOL SONG   The Company

FINALE

25. Reprise   CROSSING OFF THE   Extra children
                DAYS (Chorus)
26. Reprise   RHUBARB (Verses 6 and 8) Jen, Darbi, Venables,
                                         Temple and Extras
27. Reprise   I NEVER KNEW   Rowena, Emma, Chris,
                MATRONS HAD   and all the other children
                BIRTHDAYS (last verse)
28. Reprise   FIRE DRILL (last verse) The Company
29. Reprise   SCHOOL SONG   The Company

A piano/vocal score is available from Samuel French Ltd.

PRODUCTION NOTES

The children should appear to be between the ages of ten and fourteen, although some younger ones may be included among the extras. They are all required to sing and dance, but only DARBISHIRE and ROWENA sing complete solos. In some of the ensemble numbers, such as "THREE BOOS FOR SIR" and "CROSSING OFF THE DAYS", solo lines or verses can, if necessary, be sung by members of the cast other than those nominated in the script, thus providing scope for good singers as well as good actors. The songs and the music allow considerable opportunity for simple choreography.

The producer should bear in mind that the children of Linbury Court School are well-behaved and co-operative whenever members of the staff are present, and the disasters that occur are not the result of disruptive behaviour but rather because some well-intentioned plan has misfired.

CAST

JENNINGS is a lively, impetuous eleven-year-old, the natural leader of the group. DARBISHIRE, the same age, is an earnest, bespectacled boy, somewhat slow to comprehend, but anxious to be involved. ROWENA has the most demanding of the girls' parts. She is a loner, resentful of the interruptions to her music practice and oblivious to her shortcomings as a pianist.

VENABLES, TEMPLE, EMMA and CHRISTINE are typical examples of the *genus* "boy" or "girl" and only too ready to judge events from their own point of view. There is rivalry between them with the boys inclined to denigrate the girls, but they quickly close ranks against any alleged deprivation of their rights.

MR WILKINS is a middle-aged teacher whose authoritarian manner stems from the fact that he cannot understand the workings of the growing mind. The things children do seem fantastic when judged from his grown-up point of view. In contrast, MR CARTER and MATRON, both younger than their colleague, are always ready to lend a sympathetic ear to the children's problems. The HEADMASTER is a tolerant man whose main concern is to preserve the smooth-running of school routine. IRVING BORROWMORE is an elderly, competent professional actor with no illusions about life in the theatre.

THE SET

Ideally, the dormitory should be at a raised level, reached by a staircase and curtained off by a gauze. If this is not practicable, it can be constructed from rostra with a few steps leading up to the entrance. If space is limited, one pupil's desk, only, should be set, *down* R, for Act I. The other desks needed for Act II, Scene 1 can be brought on by children when the bell rings for afternoon school.

The electric bell-push is in frequent use as an entrance cue and in case of failure should be backed up by a duplicate bell, off stage. To ensure exact timing, the alarm clock bell must also be operated as a spot effect, off stage.

An alternative to the usual curtain call after the finale is for the curtain to rise on a tableau depicting a "send-up" of the traditional school photograph, with staff and children seated, kneeling or standing motionless, and wearing the slightly glazed expressions so often associated with photographs of this sort. The pose should be held for a few seconds only and should not be exaggerated. If the curtain call is taken in this way the actors in Shakespearean costume will make an exit before the Headmaster's final speech in order to change into school uniform for the finale.

Interrupted speeches

In some cases where the children are speaking a possible continuation of their interrupted speech is given in parenthesis after the speech to forestall any awkward moments, e.g.

Emma . . . and I'll probably become a famous musician one day, and . . .
(perhaps I'll even be asked to play at the . . .)

THE MUSIC

A lusty, chest-voiced type of singing for the children is preferable to "cathedral" voice production; the keynote of the unison singing is good attack and rhythmic drive. Mr Wilkins could avoid all singing if really necessary but in any event a "singer's" voice is not required (range bass/baritone). Mr Carter should be a light-voiced high baritone. A singing voice is really necessary for this part. The Headmaster need not sing (there is an optional part included in the Fire Drill reprise). Matron, like Carter, should have a pleasant singing voice (range mezzo soprano) and Borrowmore must sing and dance (baritone range).

There is a piano/vocal score available from Samuel French Ltd. The musical is also scored for an ensemble of 12 players:

Flute (doubling piccolo)	Oboe (doubling cor anglais)
Clarinet	Bassoon
Horn	Trombone
Two violins	Viola
Cello	Double bass
Percussion (dance kit and tympani)	

Band parts are available on hire from Samuel French.

ACT I

Linbury Court, a co-educational boarding school. Early evening, between tea and bedtime

The main acting area is a hall used for general purposes. From one side a door leads to classrooms; from the other another door leads to the dining-hall. Above the latter is an archway to the front door, staff room and other rooms in the building. Above the classroom door is a corridor to an additional wing. From the centre of the hall a staircase leads to a landing and dormitory on a raised level. The dormitory contains a sash window and four beds. The landing runs above the corridor at stage level and leads off. (See plan on p. 63.)

The hall is also used as a classroom and has a couple of pupils' desks and chairs against the wall above the classroom door. There is a piano below the dining-room door. An electric bell is in a prominent position near the corridor exit. There are challenge cups displayed, a notice-board, etc. The decor is reasonably colourful, though the room has a slightly battered appearance from being used by generations of children

MUSIC 1. *OVERTURE*

When the CURTAIN *rises, the stage is empty. In the classroom a choir is rehearsing the School Song to a piano accompaniment (recorded): verses four and five only are needed at the rise*

MUSIC 2. *SCHOOL SONG* (recorded)

1. These are the days of eager childhood
   These are the days of hopeful dreaming
   Striving with heart and soul
   To reach our goal
   And play our part.

2. Now is the time of our preparing
   Soon is our time for worthwhile service
   When action supplants our dreams
   Hope like a beacon gleams
   Steadfast and true before our eyes.
   Freely our gifts we'll share,
   Each other's burdens bear,
   United in strength to win the prize.

3. Journeying through all the years of life,
   We have a part that we must play;
   To do our best to face the fears of life,
   And help our fellow-creatures on their way.

4. Signposts pointing to the future,
   Marching onwards towards manhood,
   Ready throughout our life
   To face the strife
   With cheerful heart.

5. These are the days of eager childhood,
   These are the days of hopeful dreaming,
   Striving with heart and soul,
   Hoping to reach our goal
   Striding ahead with flag unfurled.
   Striving with might and main
   Willing to fight again,
   Hoping to make a brave, new world.

During the song Mr Wilkins enters from the classroom with a stack of exercise books and exits through the archway. Matron enters along the landing, goes into the dormitory with a pile of laundry which she leaves on a bed and then exits. The Headmaster enters from the dining-hall, pins a notice on the board and exits. Mr Carter enters from the archway, consults his watch and crosses to the corridor. These entrances and exits overlap to provide continuous movement. As the song ends Mr Carter presses the electric bell switch, holds it for ten seconds and exits through the archway. As the bell stops boys and girls swarm on stage from every entrance and down the stairs. There is lively activity and ad lib. dialogue, including imaginary engines revving, guns firing, etc

MUSIC 3. *CROSSOVER* (played as background)

Children cross the hall en route *for other rooms, carrying musical instruments, table-tennis bats, glove puppets, etc. Two girls stagger across with a guinea-pig hutch: two boys pick their way through the crowd balancing chessmen on a board. Activity continues for twenty seconds. Then the stage clears abruptly*

Music fades out

The classroom door hurtles open and Jennings runs on. Two cocoa tins jammed over his ears stick out at right angles to his head like a pair of handlebars. The tins are joined by a length of string. He removes a tin from one ear and uses it as a microphone

Jennings (*speaking into the tin*) Hullo, Earth! Hullo, Earth! Attention, all space-shipping! Moon calling Earth. Moon calling Earth. Are you receiving me? . . . This is Space-Pilot Jennings calling Jodrell Bank from Lunar Base Camp One on forty-one point five megacycles. Astronaut Darbishire and I arrived on the moon at tea-time and have been doing—er—a lot of famous exploits. Astronaut Darbishire has gone off to explore some craters by moonlight in the Lunar Exploration Module. (*He uses the tins as binoculars as though surveying the auditorium and stage*)

Chris and Emma enter down the corridor carrying a home-made snorkel of garden hose and funnels

No sign of any moon dwellers around these parts. Just a load of old stars and stripes and hammers and sickles all over the place. (*Seeing Chris and Emma through the binoculars*) Hold it, there's a couple coming out of a crater. Hostile female moon-natives by the look of them. What else now? Oh yes. Having a lovely time. Wish you were here. Hope you are well and having decent weather.

Temple enters from the classroom

Temple Hey, Jennings! Aren't you ready yet?
Jennings Ready! I've been woffling away at ninety-five decibels for the last hour-and-a-half. Couldn't you hear me?
Temple We could hear you all right *without* the radio, but we couldn't hear a thing *with* it. Try out of earshot—and out of eyesight-shot, too.

Temple exits to the classroom

Jennings goes to the archway

Chris Hey, Jennings! Want to have a go with our snorkel. Emma and I made it out of a . . . (bit of rubber tubing)
Jennings Snorkels, huh! Snorkels are *out*. It's telecommunications now.

Jennings exits throughout the archway

Emma It's always the same. By the time we get on to a new craze *they've* all gone on to something else. Look what happened when we made our biscuit-tin banjo.
Chris I know! The boys were making spectacles out of pipe-cleaners.
Emma And by the time we'd got a packet of pipe-cleaners, they were growing mustard and cress on their face flannels.
Chris And now snorkels are out. You just can't keep up, can you?
Emma It's an absolute rat race. Women's rights—huh! You don't stand a chance.

Darbishire enters along landing past the dormitory. He wears a skateboard crash-helmet surmounted by a flashing red torch-bulb. From the top of the stairs he makes a survey through a makeshift cardboard telescope and proceeds downstairs with an exaggerated gait, lifting arms and legs high as though coping with a tendency to weightlessness

Darbishire Bleep-bleep! Bleep-bleep!
Chris What's the matter with you, Darbishire?

Darbishire (*descending the stairs*) I'm practically weightless. There's hardly any gravity on the moon, you know. You can jump ever so high. (*He tries vainly to demonstrate*) Higher than that, of course. (*He comes down*) And there's no air either. You daren't take your space helmet off, even at meal times.

Chris Well, if there's no air, how do people talk to each other?

Darbishire They have little balloons floating over their heads with conversation in them.

Chris M'yes, I suppose that'd work all right, if the balloons were airtight.

Jennings enters from the archway

Darbishire Oh hullo, Jen. Made contact with Jodrell Bank yet?

Jennings Yes, I could hear Atkinson as clear as a bell.

Darbishire What did he say?

Jennings Well, I couldn't actually hear any words, but it was ever so loud. Like to have a go?

Darbishire Thanks.

Jennings and Darbishire move down and fiddle with the equipment. Jennings puts on the helmet

Chris I vote we scrap our snorkel. It's out of date already.

Emma You mean switch over to telecommunications and satellites? Cocoa tins, the lot?

Chris It's our only chance to get in on the space race. We've got to keep up for the sake of women's prestige.

Emma Yes, of course. Hey, Jennings, can Chris and I have a go next?

Jennings Sorry, Emma. This is a job for the boys. You don't have female astronauts.

Emma (*to Chris*) There you are, you see! It's a man's world.

Chris It you can't beat them—join them.

Emma But they won't let you join them.

Chris Okay, then you'll have to beat them.

Emma How?

Chris They may get it all their own way down on Earth, but you just wait till they get into outer space. They'll find women planet dwellers more than a match for weedy Earthmen. (*Going*) Come on!

Emma Where to?

Chris To round up the female planetary army, of course.

Chris and Emma exit along the corridor

Jennings hands the cocoa tins to Darbishire and runs into the classroom. He turns in the doorway

Jennings (*calling back*) Okay. You're tuned in to Earth. Start your message now.

Darbishire opens his mouth to speak, and is overcome by shyness

Go on, Darbi. They're waiting.

Darbishire (*covering the mouthpiece with his hand and shouting back in a panic-stricken whisper*) I can't think of anything to say.
Jennings It doesn't matter what. Sing a song or something.

Jennings exits to the classroom

MUSIC 4. *FAMOUS FIRST WORDS*

Darbishire   1. Does anyone here know the dialling code
To ring up the Earth from the Moon?
It's a long-distance call and I haven't much change
I know the pips will start a-buzzing all too soon.

2. I want to get through to Mission Control
If they're willing to pay for the call
For I'm sure all people that on earth do dwell
Would like to know we're alive—and well
And they're waiting for a message that will stir all hearts
And go down in hist—in history.

3. So sharpen your pencils: tune in your transistors
Here is the news from Outer Space
I'm just going to broadcast some famous first words
To the whole of the hu—hu—human race.

4. When first I stepped out on this cold, frozen landscape
The words flashed into my mind.
"It's a short step forward for little old me
But a great leap for mankind."
It's a short step forward for little old me
But a great leap for—leap for mankind.

Mr Wilkins enters through the archway from the staff room. He crosses towards the staircase

Darbishire Testing for sound. Next verse coming up.
Mr Wilkins (*softly*) Darbishire!
Darbishire (*turning in confusion*) Oh sir, Mr Wilkins, sir. Sorry, sir, I didn't see you, sir.
Mr Wilkins Are you feeling all right?
Darbishire Yes, sir.
Mr Wilkins What are you talking to yourself for?
Darbishire I wasn't sir. I was talking to someone down on Earth—I mean, in the classroom; or, rather—I'm on the Moon, you see. Not really, of course. Just pretending.
Mr Wilkins Are you, indeed!
Darbishire Yes, sir. Jennings thinks there may be people in outer space, you see. Special little men with green faces and eight arms and legs and things like television aerials coming out of their heads.
Mr Wilkins Jennings *would*!

Darbishire So we're on this expedition, you see, to teach them to be civilized and speak English, and—er—how to play football and things.

Mr Wilkins You'd have a job teaching that lot to play football. They'd need four pairs of boots each, to begin with, and they'd puncture the ball every time they tried to head it.

Darbishire Well, you know what I mean, sir. We want to bring them peace and goodwill and brotherly love and all that sort of flannel.

Mr Wilkins I suggest you leave the inhabitants of outer space to their own devices and try spreading a little peace and goodwill amongst the members of Form Three. This space travel nonsense is getting completely out of hand. Every time I turn a corner I bump into silly little boys with smudges of green chalk on their faces, spluttering and gargling ridiculous rocket noises. (*He gives a disparaging imitation*) Voom—voom—voom.   Dacka—dacka—dacka.   Kik-kik-kik-kik. Chigga-chigga-chigga-chigga.

Darbishire (*admiringly*) Coo, you're jolly good at it, sir.

Mr Wilkins Eh! Well, I've had just about enough of it. And if there's any more nonsense about green-faced planet-dwellers tearing round the building making a hideous din I shall—I shall . . . Well, there'd better not *be* any more nonsense, that's all.

Darbishire We'll be ever so quiet, sir.

Mr Wilkins exits up the stairs

MUSIC 4a. *FAMOUS FIRST WORDS* (reprise)

Darbishire   5. The whole world is waiting; the whole world's pulsating,
It's the sensation of the year.
It's the chance of a lifetime to bring you the news
From the strato-strato-strato stratosphere.

6. When first I stepped out on this cold, frozen landscape
The words flashed into my mind:
"It's a short step forward for little old me
But a great leap for mankind"
It's a short step forward for little old me
But a great leap for—leap for mankind.

Jennings enters from the classroom, pursued by Emma, Chris and extra Girls wearing green netting vegetable bags over their heads. Emma wears a plastic goldfish bowl as a space helmet

Jennings Help, help! I'm being chased by a gang of hostile female planet dwellers. Hide me, Darbi!

The extra Girls surround Jennings and Darbishire, push them down into sitting position, back to back, and imprison them under a string hammock

Girls Earthmen, go home! Earthmen, go home! Earthmen, out, out, out!

Chris (*with a bogus Red Indian accent*) Me, Big Chief Moonshine, mighty famous Greenskin! Me make Earthman Paleface bite pumice dust.

Girls Down with the Earthmen!

Chris Me give Earthmen famous lunar treatment.

MUSIC 5. EARTHMAN, GO HOME!

Emma ⎫
Chris ⎬ 1. We who dwell in outer spaces
Girls ⎭   Venus, Mars and similar places,
        You can tell us by the traces
        Of the green chalk upon our faces.
        We all say to Earthman:
        Go home,
        We don't want you here.
        So blast off—back home!

Emma ⎱
Chris ⎰ 2. Earthman has no right on Moon
        Send him packing plenty soon,
        If not now, this afternoon.
        We pay the piper, call the tune.
        Planet dwellers all say:
All   Go home,
        We don't want you here
        So blast off—back home!

Emma 3. When Earthman touch down here, he tell Mission Control,
        The Moon is deserted, we can't find a soul,
        But!

Emma ⎱
Chris ⎰ 4. Moonmen hide in nearest crater
        Flee from sonic oscillator.
        No like Earthman infiltrator.
        Going to ground now—see you later!
        Later on, when we say:
All   Go home,
        We don't want you here
        So blast off—back home!

Emma 5. Folk of stratospheric races,
        Sprouting legs in numerous places,
Chris   Signs of elephantiasis,
        Weightless trousers—look, no braces!
Both   Stand fast by our watchword:
All   Go home,
        We don't want you here
        So blast off—back home!

Chris 6. Our life was so tranquil, though just a bit boring,
        But all that has altered, now earthman's exploring.

Emma ⎱
Chris ⎰ 7. We don't want your H-bomb banger,
        Go before you drop a clanger,
        We'd rather have an orang-utang, or
        Any old monkey than a man, for—
All   We claim squatters' rights.
        No more lunar flights.

All   8. We who dwell in outer spaces
Venus, Mars and similar places,
You can tell us by the traces
Of the green chalk upon our faces.
Altogether shout:
Get out, get out, get out!
Astronauts not welcome,
Get out of space!

As the song ends Venables, Temple and extra Boys enter from the corridor

Venables Rescue! Astronauts to the rescue!
Temple Up the earthmen! Down with the female planet dwellers!
Boys Dacka—dacka—dacka—dacka . . .

The extra Boys put the extra Girls to rout, and chase after them. There is uproar as they exit in all directions. Mr Wilkins enters unobserved at the top of the staircase as Jennings, Darbishire, Venables, Temple, Emma and Chris continue hostilities on stage. Some extra Children remain to take part in the song "Three Boos for Sir"

Mr Wilkins (*shouting*) Silence!

The uproar ceases as children see Mr Wilkins on the staircase

I have never in all my life heard such a disgraceful pandemonium. You know perfectly well that you're not allowed to play noisy games in this part of the building.
All Yes, sir. (*They start moving back to the classroom door*)
Mr Wilkins (*sharply*) Stay where you are!

They stop. Mr Wilkins with great dignity descends the stairs and comes down

He stands looking at them in a silence designed to instil awe

Almost unnoticed, Rowena sidles in from the dining-hall carrying some sheets of music and sits at the piano. She is unconscious of what is occurring elsewhere

(*After a pause*) Now listen to me, all of you. Listen carefully. I have something very important to say.

Rowena thumps out first few bars of "The Merry Peasant". Mr Wilkins wheels round angrily

What—what on earth! Stop that horrible noise, Rowena!
Rowena Oh, but sir, Mrs Hind said I'd got to do my practice before bed-time, sir.
Mr Wilkins Not now, girl, not now.
Rowena But sir, Mrs Hind *said*. It's for the concert, you see, and . . .
Mr Wilkins All right, but not here. Go somewhere else.
Rowena But, sir, there isn't . . . (anywhere else)

Mr Wilkins Oh, for goodness sake! Well, keep quiet when I'm talking, then.

Rowena Yes, sir.

Mr Wilkins Now, what was I saying? Oh yes. This ridiculous craze for space travel games has got completely out of hand, and it's got to stop. Look at the state you're in! Tuck your shirt in, Venables!

Venables does so

Now, I'm warning you. If you boys and girls can't find some quieter way of spending your free time between now and the end of term you'll find me far more dangerous to cope with than any green-faced monster from the planet Pluto. Is that understood?

All Yes sir.

Mr Wilkins Right! And now I suggest you all find some hobby that doesn't involve shattering the eardrums of the staff in all your waking moments.

Mr Wilkins exits up the stairs and along the landing

Rowena joins the other children

Venables Coo, jolly mouldy swizzle. That puts paid to our space programme. Just leaves Russia and America with a clear field.

Temple What else can you expect from an earthbound character like Old Wilkie! Tt! Three boos for Sir.

MUSIC 6.   THREE BOOS FOR SIR

All (*speaking*) Boo! Boo! Boo!

All	1.	Three boos for Sir
Jennings		Masters have got no sense of justice
All		Three boos for Sir
Jennings		Now you can see why our mistrust is
		Aimed at a pedagogue who
		Growls like an angry dog who
		Bites as well as barks,
		Hoping to leave some marks.
All	2.	Three boos for Sir
Chris		Masters are sometimes most unfair
All		Three boos for Sir
Chris		They blow their top and tear their hair,
		Creating a situation
		Without any provocation
		Rant and roar and shout
		Throw their weight about.
Emma	3.	Recently,
		I behaved decently,
		I did my best to humour all the staff.
		I was polite to them,

I said good night to them;
And when they made their ghastly jokes
I did my best to laugh.

All   4. Three boos for Sir
Darbishire   Even in most enlightened schools
All   Three boos for Sir
Darbishire   Masters will always break the rules,
They do what they tell you not to,
And not as they say you've got to,
But if you make a fuss;
(*Speaking*) "Rules don't apply to us!"

All   5. Three boos for Sir,
Don't shed any tears for Wilkie's sake.
Three boos for Sir
His job is just a piece of cake,
Strutting round giving orders
Moaning at all the boarders.
Rowena   If ever the chance occurs,
I'd like a job like Sir's.

Rowena   6. Give me
The opportunity
To run a school where girls are in control.
And the teachers
God's lowliest creatures
Are made to toe the line and jolly well do what they're told.

All   7. Three boos for Sir
Masters are sometimes most unfair
Three boos for Sir
They blow their top and tear their hair,
Creating a situation
Without any provocation
Rant and roar and shout
Throw their weight about.

All   8. Three boos for Sir
Girls   The trouble with teachers when they teach
All   Three boos for Sir
Girls   They never practise what they preach,
Boys   They say: Take our advice, boys
Be quiet as little mice, boys
Eat up your prunes and rice, boys
It's really rather nice, boys.
All   But whatever you do, whatever you do,
You're sure to be wrong if you do as they do.
Never do as they do—
Always do as they say,
And keep out of their way!

The extra Children exit. Mr Carter enters from the archway carrying letters and a parcel

The children rush towards him

Darbishire Oh sir, are you giving the post out? Goodo!

Venables Anything for me? Venables, sir.

Temple Anything for Temple, sir?

Mr Carter If you'll all stop crowding round me like bees round a honey-pot I'll have a look. (*He sorts the post*) One for you, Christine.

Chris Coo, thank you. (*She takes a letter*)

Mr Carter Nothing for the rest of you . . . (*Looking at the parcel*) Oh yes. C. E. J. Darbishire.

Darbishire Coo, thank you, sir. (*He examines the parcel*) It's my god-mother sir. I recognize her hand.

Emma You're crazy. She couldn't be that shape unless she'd been cremated.

Darbishire Her handwriting, you clodpoll. I bet I know what it is, too. It's a cake.

Emma Better hurry up and eat it then. Only two more days to the end of the term.

Darbishire I shan't waste it, don't you worry. I've got a scheme.

Mr Carter Extraordinary headgear, Emma! A new fashion?

Emma It was my space helmet, only Mr Wilkins says we're not allowed to play any more. He says it makes too much noise.

Mr Carter It certainly does. The patter of little feet when the planet-dwellers are on the warpath sounds like a herd of buffalo stampeding across the plain.

Chris But we must do *something*, sir. It's so boring waiting for the end of term with nothing to do.

Mr Carter I should say there's plenty to do if you use your gumption. What about the concert on Friday? Any of you lot performing?

Rowena I am, sir. I'm doing my piano solo. I'm hoping it'll be my big chance to break into show business.

Mr Carter Good for you. And the rest of you?

Jennings We haven't really thought about it yet, sir.

Mr Carter Start thinking now. It needn't be anything elaborate. Just a scene from Shakespeare or something like that.

Venables Oh no, sir—not Shakespeare. Couldn't we write something ourselves?

Mr Carter Such as?

Jennings We could—er—we could write a play about a man with a moustache.

Mr Carter Why?

Jennings Because Darbishire's got one—haven't you Darbi.

Darbishire produces a large black false moustache from his pocket and attaches it

Darbishire Bags I wear it, then.

Jennings You can wear it in Scene One: and then you could get shot or something so someone else can wear it in Scene Two.

Temple Me, for instance. (*He grabs the moustache and puts it on*) I could be a detective with a moustache who's called in to investigate the murder in Scene Three.

Venables (*grabbing the moustache*) And then you could get bumped off so I could come on wearing it in Scene Four. Come on, let's go to the library and get it all written out.

The Children go towards the corridor with Jennings in the lead. Mr Carter goes to the notice-board to consult the lists

Chris Can we come, too?

Venables You can if you like, but you'll be wasting your time. There won't be any parts for women with moustaches.

The Headmaster enters from the corridor

Jennings, swinging his arms, collides with the Headmaster, the others stop and give way

Jennings Oh, sir. I'm terribly sorry, sir. I didn't think you'd be coming in just then, sir.

Headmaster You didn't think! Surely I have the right to walk freely about the building without being used as a buffer by clumsy little boys.

Jennings Oh yes, sir, of course, sir.

Headmaster Whereas you, Jennings, have no right at all to go charging about like a bull in a china shop.

Jennings No, sir. No right at all, sir. I didn't mean to hit you, though. I was just practising my in-swingers.

Headmaster Your what?

Jennings Well they're not *really* in-swingers. More like off-breaks actually, sir.

Headmaster Off-breaks! A somewhat unseasonable occupation I should have thought. However! Go and find Mr Wilkins and ask him if he can spare me a moment.

Jennings Mr Wilkins, sir. Yes, sir. He went that-a-way, sir.

Jennings runs upstairs

The others exit along the corridor

Headmaster Off-breaks, h'm. (*He shuffles forward and swings his arm as though bowling, becomes aware that Carter is watching, and changes the movement to indicate a stiff muscle*) Ah, Carter! Touch of rheumatism, I fancy.

Jennings (*running off along the landing, shouting*) Sir! Sir! Mr Wilkins! Sir! Urgent message, sir. The Head wants you at once, sir.

Jennings exits

Headmaster I think most of our arrangements for the end of term are

proceeding smoothly, but there are one or two matters that I'd like to
discuss. The children's travelling arrangements, for example.

Mr Carter I've attended to all that, Headmaster. It's all in order.

Headmaster Splendid. Splendid.

Jennings appears on landing at top of stairs

As you know, Wilkins is leaving this term to . . . (*He glances up and sees
Jennings*)

Jennings reacts to the information he has just heard

Headmaster What is it, Jennings?

Jennings (*shattered*) Er—nothing, sir. That is, I didn't know that about
Mr Wilkins, sir.

Headmaster What about Mr Wilkins?

Jennings Only that I never thought—well, anyway, I've told him you want
him, sir. He's coming now.

Jennings exits along the landing

Headmaster Now what was I saying?

Mr Carter I think I must have misunderstood you. What you actually
said was "Wilkins is leaving this term". You couldn't have meant that.

Headmaster (*nonplussed*) I said he was leaving! That's ridiculous, Carter.
I'm quite sure I never . . . Oh! Oh, I see. (*He laughs at the absurdity of
the misunderstanding*) Yes, of course. What I was saying was that this
term Wilkins is leaving by the *early train* on Saturday morning as he's
joining a ski-ing party who are setting off for the Continent at midday.
(*He laughs again*) Yes, he's leaving all right, but he's coming back again
next term. All the better for his holiday, I trust!

Mr Wilkins appears on the landing

Mr Wilkins You want to see me, H.M.?

Headmaster Just a few end-of-term routine matters. I don't think you've
given me your reports yet.

Mr Wilkins (*coming downstairs*) I've done them all except for Form Three.
Really, that form's sending my hair grey. Can't behave, will talk, won't
work, must fidget.

Mr Carter Oh surely! They're not as bad as all that.

Mr Wilkins If you ask me, Carter, they're a lot worse than all that.

Headmaster I must admit I'm far from satisfied with their progress. High
time that form pulled its socks up.

*Matron enters from the dining-hall with a bundle of towels and goes
towards the stairs*

Mr Wilkins Especially that boy, Jennings. He's the most scatter-brained . . .

Headmaster Ah, Matron. I believe you had some query about the little
—ah—informal entertainment that the children are putting on for the
staff.

Matron I'd like to know what they're planning to do. There's always a
headlong stampede to the linen room to sort out costumes ten minutes

before the curtain goes up, so if I could have some idea . . .

Headmaster Yes, of course. You know the programme, don't you Carter?

Mr Carter If you can call it that. Just a hotch-potch of items really. (*He produces a list from his pocket*) Let's see now, we've got various piano and violin solos, the Form One percussion band, Form Two girls' country dancing, the choir are doing some songs. That's about all . . . Oh, there is one last-minute addition to the programme. A group of third-formers are hoping to do a short play.

Headmaster Splendid. I'm all in favour of the children organizing the whole thing themselves—except, of course, when parents are present. And what is this—ah—dramatic opus that they're going to charm us with?

Mr Carter It's a play about a moustache.

Headmaster I beg your pardon?

Mr Carter They're writing it themselves. They've got a moustache which they're all anxious to wear, so as one character gets killed off, another inherits this vital stage property.

Headmaster Is that the plot?

Mr Carter As I understand it, yes.

Mr Wilkins Typical Form Three!

Headmaster No, Carter, it's too ridiculous. We can't sit through this sort of puerile pantomime from the pen of Form Three. Too embarrassing for words.

Mr Carter They're very keen, you know.

Headmaster I dare say, but I'm not having it. They must choose something more suitable—a scene from Shakespeare, for example. Surely we can find something better than a play about an inherited moustache.

Mr Carter All right, I'll tell them.

Headmaster H'm I wonder now! What was the name of that actor—fellow who came down the term before last and did those dramatic recitations? You remember, Carter: character studies from Dickens and Shakespeare and that sort of thing.

Mr Carter You mean Irving Borrowmore?

Headmaster That's the chap. Very good he was, too. I think I'll give him a ring and see if he's free. What do you think, Wilkins?

Mr Wilkins I'm all for it. Anything to save the concert from being the non-event of the term.

Headmaster Well, I mustn't waste time. All Form Five's Latin marks to add up yet. (*He goes to the archway*) And you'll let me have those reports as soon as possible, Wilkins?

Mr Wilkins I'll do them right away.

The Headmaster exits through the archway

MUSIC 7. *THE THINGS THEY DO*

A play about a moustache. Tt! Silly little boys. I just don't understand the way their tiny minds work.

1. I've always said that boys are hard to understand,
    The things they choose to do are quite absurd, don't you
    agree?
    The more I try to fathom out the reasons for their
    foolishness
    The more obscure their motives seem to be.
    They reach such heights of puerile lunacy;
    They plumb the depths of imbecility.
    Perhaps it's me! Maybe I'm dense
    But I can't see a grain of sense
    In the stupid things that children like to do.

Matron 2. It's not like that at all. Can't you understand.
    The things they do make perfect sense to them—if not
    to you.
    The reason you're so puzzled and so baffled and
    bewildered
    Is because you've got the grown-up point of view.
    Just take a look inside the growing mind:
    The answers are all there for you to find.
    Don't let yourself be driven frantic
    By some harmless, childish antic
    Try to see life through a youthful pair of eyes.

Mr Wilkins (*speaking*) Yes, but all the same . . .

Mr Carter 3. You'd do well to think—of the dinosaur,
    A prehistoric creature who was too set in his ways,
    He couldn't face the changes that were going on around
    him,
    So he died! Resisting progress never pays.
    So open up your mind to new ideas
    That's my advice to those of riper years.
    Though these youngsters baffle you
    It's a stage they must go through
    They will grow up into people all too soon.

Mr Wilkins 4. That's all very well! They're monsters all the same
    For civilized behaviour they just couldn't care a hoot.
    For instance, they will get their fingers smeared with
    sticky toffee
    Then deal a pack of cards—or play the flute*
    The way they carry on's a sheer disgrace,
    They're barely members of the human race.

Mr Carter ⎫ Don't exaggerate their errors
Matron   ⎬ They're not really little terrors
              ⎭ They're the same as you and I were at their age.

---

* *Mr Wilkins absently places his hand on piano top and removes it with a playing card adhering.*

Mr Wilkins (*speaking*) I'd better make a start on those reports, I suppose.

Mr Wilkins exits through the archway to the staff room

Matron And I've got all the laundry to check before I can even start on packing the children's trunks. (*She moves to the stairs and starts to go up*)

Darbishire, Venables and Temple enter at a run from the corridor. Venables is wearing the moustache

Venables Sir, please sir, Mr Carter sir, may we borrow that starting pistol you use for the sports. You see we've got to shoot Darbishire in Scene One so Jennings can have the moustache in Scene Two.

Mr Carter Sorry, it's all off. The Head doesn't like the sound of your play.

Boys Oh sir!

Mr Carter He'd rather you did a scene from Shakespeare instead.

Darbishire I suppose we *could*, if we had to. Did Hamlet have a moustache sir?

Mr Carter I don't think so.

Darbishire Well that washes Hamlet out, thank goodness.

Temple Perhaps we could do the murder of Julius Caesar with the starting pistol. Brutus or someone could wear the moustache.

Mr Carter No, Temple. And I suggest you stop trying to fit Shakespeare into your false moustache. Never mind the properties—the play's the thing.

Darbishire Which play sir?

Mr Carter Well, what about that passage from *Henry the Fifth* that you were reading in class with Mr Wilkins.

Temple Oh, but we couldn't do that, sir, we haven't got any costumes.

Matron If there aren't too many of you in it I expect I could find something for you to wear.

Venables Oh Matron, would you really? That'd be super!

Darbishire Real costumes, wow! We'd need helmets and cloaks and armour and things.

Matron I'll see what I can do.

Darbishire Thanks, Matron. Hey, Temple, if we do that scene about Agincourt we can burst paper bags for the cannon balls going off in the background.

Venables Can we come and get our costumes now, Matron?

Matron Give me a chance. I haven't made them yet. You'd better get the play ready first.

Darbishire Yes, of course. Good old Matron! Good old Shakespeare! Let's go and get the *Henry the Fifth* books and have a look at it.

Matron goes upstairs and exits along the landing

The Boys make for the door to the classroom, declaiming at the top of their voices

Venables ⎤ "To be or not to be, that is the question."
Darbishire ⎬ "Friends, Romans and countrymen, lend me your ears."
Temple ⎦ "Once more unto the breach, dear friends, once more."

The Boys exit. Mr Wilkins enters from the archway with a folder of reports.
He reacts to the uproar at the classroom door

Mr Wilkins What in the name of thunder is going on now?
Mr Carter Just getting ready for the concert.
Mr Wilkins If they can't do it without making all that noise it'd be better
to scrap the thing altogether.
Mr Carter Oh, I don't know. You must agree it's an improvement on the
outer space exploration craze.
Mr Wilkins You can say that again. Still, that's all over now. I've put a
stop to all that tomfoolery in no uncertain manner.

Emma and Chris enter along the corridor. Emma is still wearing the in-
verted goldfish bowl on her head. They confer in whispers upstage

Mr Wilkins The space race is over as far as these children are concerned.
They know that when I say a thing I mean it.
Mr Carter Yes, of course.
Mr Wilkins You have me to thank for the fact that there'll be no more
astronauts and planet-dwellers charging about the building in fantastic
headgear and . . . (*Seeing Emma*) What—what on earth!
Mr Carter Take it off at once, Emma, before it gets broken.
Emma I can't. It won't come.
Chris We both tried and it's no good.

Mr Wilkins stands above Emma and tries to ease the bowl

Mr Wilkins Yes, yes, yes, but what did you want to put the thing *on* for
in the first place, you silly little girl?
Emma I only wanted to see if it would fit.
Mr Wilkins Fit! See if it would fit? You must be off your head. Civilized
people don't do things like that. You never see Mr Carter or me going
round sticking our heads into glass cases to see if they fit, do you?
Emma No, sir.

Rowena enters along the corridor with her music. She crosses above the
group and sits at the piano

Mr Carter Let me have a go.

Mr Carter takes over from Mr Wilkins

Mr Carter H'm. You've got yourself in a spot this time, haven't you,
Emma?
Emma I was just pretending it was a planet-dweller's space helmet.
Mr Wilkins (*outraged*) Doh! I might have known. All this tomfoolery!
You silly little girl.
Mr Carter It's coming. Five-four-three-two-one-zero. We have lift-off!
(*He removes the bowl*) There we are.
Emma Thank you, sir.

Chris Success! Success!

Emma Thank you very *much*, sir. Thank you very much *indeed* sir.

Mr Carter All right, all right. Consider it said. (*He places the bowl on a desk*)

Mr Wilkins It is *not* all right, if you don't mind my saying so, Mr Carter. These nonsensical crazes have . . . Now listen to me, you girls. Listen carefully.

Rowena having sorted out her music, thumps out opening bars of "The Merry Peasant". Mr Wilkins swivels round in exasperation

Mr Wilkins Doh! Stop that horrible noise, Rowena!

Rowena But, sir, Mrs Hind said . . .

Mr Wilkins I don't care if the Archbishop of Canterbury said. I told you to go and do your practice somewhere else.

Rowena But there isn't anywhere else free, and Mrs Hind *did* say . . .

Mr Wilkins Out, girl, out!

Rowena Yes, sir.

Rowena gathers up her music and exits upstairs and along the landing

Mr Wilkins Now what was I saying. (*He turns back to Emma*) Well, anyway I've already made the position quite clear, so you two had better make yourselves scarce before I say any more.

Emma Yes, sir. Please may we take the . . . (*She indicates the bowl, but Mr Wilkins is in no mood to listen*)

Mr Wilkins You heard what I said! Out! Double quick!

Emma Yes, sir.

Chris and Emma exit to the classroom

Mr Wilkins Tt, tt, tt! Honestly, Carter! (*He picks up bowl, and mimics Emma*) "I only wanted to see if it would fit." Tt! I ask you. Where did the silly little girl get this flower vase or whatever it is, anyway? I don't remember seeing it about the place.

Matron enters along the landing and calls from the head of the stairs

Matron Oh, Mr Carter.

Mr Carter Yes, Matron?

Matron Something rather odd seems to be happening in the girls' bathroom. One of the wash-basins is full of fish.

Mr Carter *Dead* fish?

Matron Oh no. Very much alive. Goldfish swimming up and down and having a whale of a time.

Mr Wilkins Goldfish! (*He looks at the bowl he is holding*)

Matron I can't think what's happened.

Mr Carter I can.

Mr Wilkins So can I.

Mr Carter (*taking the bowl from Mr Wilkins and starting to climb the stairs*) All right, Matron, I'll cope with this.

Mr Wilkins Doh! Space helmets, indeed! I'll teach them to turn the bath-room into an aquarium.

Mr Wilkins exits to the classroom, calling loudly

(*Off*) Christine! Emma! You there, Darbishire and you others go and find Christine and Emma for me, at once! Quickly now. Don't just stand there.

Mr Carter (*on the landing*) You haven't got a butterfly net, have you? It's going to be a job getting them back.

Matron I've got a coffee-strainer, if that's any good.

Mr Carter and Matron exit along the landing. After a moment Chris and Emma enter from corridor. They look round furtively

Chris It's all right. Old Wilkie's gone. Come on, let's get it quick before . . . Oh fish-hooks, it's disappeared.

Emma It can't have. (*She looks round the room*)

Chris We *must* find it. They won't half be fed up if we don't get them back in their bowl by bedtime.

Emma So will I. It's my wash-basin.

Darbishire and Venables enter from the classroom

Darbishire Hey, Old Sir's looking for you two.

Emma Oh goodness!

Venables I'd keep away from the launching-site if I were you. He's just about to go into orbit.

Temple enters from the classroom

Temple Hey, you're wanted you two.

Darbishire ⎱
Venables ⎰ They know. ⎱ *Speaking together*
Temple What's it all about, anyway?

Chris Our space helmet. We were going to make a space-ship, you see, and fit it up with a home-made telephone and everything.

Venables Forget it. You're a hundred years out of date. Space-ships and telephones are old hat. We're on to something new now. Shakespeare for the concert.

Chris We've had our chips again, Emma. Just can't keep up with the latest.

Emma I know. It's an absolute rat race.

Rowena appears on the landing

Rowena Hey, Chris, Emma!

Boys (*in chorus, derisively*) Mr Wilkins is looking for you!

Rowena No, not Mr Wilkins—Mr Carter. He's fishing in the bathroom.

Emma (*moving to the stairs*) Come on then. Better go and sort it out before Sir starts panicking.

Chris and Emma exit along the landing. Rowena comes down the stairs and sits at the piano

Temple Coo, I'm hungry. Have you started your cake yet, Darbi?
Darbishire No, I'm saving it for tonight. In the dorm after lights out.
Venables Jolly good!
Darbishire I hereby invite all members of our dormitory to a famous
furtive feast at midnight tonight—well, say about nine o'clock. When
the coast's clear.
Temple Jolly generous of you.
Darbishire Us three and old Jennings, so there'll be masses each. I've got
it all worked out. I shall smuggle ye famous cake up to the dorm when
we go to bed, and hide it somewhere till Matron's called silence and
gone downstairs.
Temple Good old Darbi!

Rowena starts playing. The Boys react

Boys Oh no! Not now for heaven's sake! Put a sock in it! Give it a rest!
Rowena (*rising*) Philistines! Rotten old Philistines, the lot of you!

*Rowena exits to the dining-hall as Jennings enters along the landing and
calls over the banisters*

Jennings I say, listen, you lot. What d'you think? Stop press news!
Venables If you mean old Darbi's cake, it's stale. He's just told us.
Darbishire My cake isn't stale!
Jennings No, nothing like that. Much more exciting. A supersonic
shattering shock.
Temple Go on then, what is it?
Jennings I'll tell you. Mr Wilkins is leaving!

The Boys react in amazement

Venables ⎫ What! You're pulling our legs!   ⎫
Temple   ⎬ I don't believe it!   ⎬ *Speaking together*
Darbishire ⎭ It's impossible! Old Wilkie leaving! ⎭
Jennings (*coming downstairs*) Honestly, it's true. I heard the Head telling
Mr Carter all about it. And he sent me to find Mr Wilkins at once, so
that proves it.
Venables I can't believe it. Old Wilkie leaving the school after all these
years.
Temple No more English tests. Hooray, Hooray.
Jennings Are you joking! We'll have someone else in his place next term.
Temple I hadn't thought of that. We might even get someone a lot worse.
Jenning I vote we buy him a present, just to show how sorry we are.
Boys Good scheme. Jolly good wheeze.
Darbishire I'll give five p.
Venables So will I.
Jennings Okay then. I'll go round and rake in donations from all the
people in our form tomorrow, and on Thursday I'll get permission from
Mr Carter to go down to the village and buy a present. How's that?

The Boys raise their hands in assent

That's settled, then. And in the meantime I vote we all decide to be specially decent to old Wilkie because it's his last few days at Linbury.

Venables How can we be more decent to him than we are already?

Jennings Oh, lots of ways. Open the door for him when he goes out of the room.

Venables I always do that, anyway.

Jenings Well, open it wider then. And laugh whenever he cracks a joke.

Mr Carter enters from the landing, descends stairs and goes to the bell-push

Venables I usually do.

Jennings Well, laugh louder. I know his jokes are chronic, but you can laugh in a good cause, can't you?

Mr Carter rings the bell, holding it for some seconds

Temple Dorm bell. Don't forget your cake, Darbishire.

Darbishire Goodness no. I'll go and get it.

Darbishire exits to the classroom as the extra Boys and Girls come out chattering, cross the hall and join Jennings and the others who lead the way upstairs

MUSIC 8. *CROSSOVER*

Matron appears on the top landing, goes into the dormitory and switches on the lights

Mr Carter stands at the foot of the stairs replying to "Good night, sir" from all the Children as they ascend. Jennings, Venables and Temple go into the dormitory and start undressing. Venables sleeps nearest the door, then Darbishire, Temple and Jennings

The others exit along the landing. Darbishire enters from the classroom carrying the unwrapped cake tin. He sees Mr Carter at the foot of the stairs and conceals the tin under his pullover, moving the bulge from front to back to avoid discovery as Mr Carter says "Good night". Mr Carter exits through the archway

The music fades. Darbishire mounts the stairs, sees that Matron is in the dormitory, and hovers on the threshold. The other Boys remove shirts and pullovers and put on dressing-gowns

Rowena, in a dressing-gown, approaches along the landing

Rowena Matron, Matron! Emergency, Matron. I've run out of toothpaste.

Matron Catastrophe! Won't it wait till the morning?

Rowena No, Matron, because I've got to get up early to do my practice. I've got to get it right in time for the concert because it's my chance to . . .

Matron All right, I'll get you some.

Rowena exits along the landing

Matron follows, and sees Darbishire hovering

Hurry up, Darbishire. The others are half undressed by now.

Matron goes off

Darbishire Yes, Matron. (*He hurries into the room, stands on his bed and produces the cake tin*) Here we are, look. Ye famous cake. Where shall we hide it?

Venables Under the bedclothes, I'd say.

Jennings That's hopeless. She'd see it bulging. We've got to think of some foolproof place where Matron couldn't possibly find it.

Temple There isn't anywhere.

Jennings I know! Fabulous wheeze! (*He takes the tin from Darbishire and a linen bag from beside Temple's bed*) We'll use Temple's dirty old clothes bag.

Venables What for?

Jennings To put the cake in. Then we'll hang it out of the window on a piece of string. (*He puts the tin in the linen bag*)

Darbishire But it's no good to us if it's hanging out of the window all night.

Jennings Only till she puts the light out. Then we pull it in and heigh-ho for ye famous feast.

Venables Yes, good scheme.

Venables opens the window and Jennings lowers the linen bag into space and then pulls sash down to hold one end of the draw-string on the window-sill

Jennings There. It holds it in place like a house on fire. No one would ever notice this bit of string on the inside, would they?

Darbishire You're an absolute genius, Jen. How d'you think of these things?

Jennings They just come bubbling up in my think-tank. It's a gift I suppose.

Rowena enters running along the landing, and looks into the dormitory

Rowena Hey, watch it! Mr Wilkins is heading this way.

Rowena exits along the landing

Jennings Don't say anything about his present if he comes in. It's got to be a secret.

Temple Yes, of course.

Jennings And all be specially decent to him, as we arranged.

Venables Okay.

Mr Wilkins enters from the landing

Mr Wilkins Come along now, you boys. Time you were in the bathroom.

Boys Yes, sir. Rather, sir. (*Flurry of undressing*)

Mr Wilkins And hurry up. I'm tired of standing about in draughty dormitories.

Darbishire You're tired, sir? Would you like to sit down? You can sit on my bed, if you like.

Venables No, sir, sit on mine. It's not so lumpy as Darbishire's.

Mr Wilkins (*baffled*) What—what . . . ?

Jennings Would you like the door closed, sir?

Mr Wilkins The door closed?

Jennings You said it was draughty, sir. Close the door, Venables. Mr Wilkins will catch cold if he stands in a draught.

Mr Wilkins I—I—I . . . What on earth are you silly little boys talking about? I'm quite capable of catching cold for myself, thank you. And if you don't move a bit faster, Jennings, you'll catch it *hot*.

Jennings Oh sir, was that meant to be a joke?

Mr Wilkins Well, no—er—that is . . .

Jennings I say, did you hear that, you chaps? Mr Wilkins has made a supersonic joke. (*He signals to the others to react*)

Boys Jolly good, sir. (*Roars of laughter*)

Temple That was funny, sir. I wish I could think of witty answers like that, don't you, Venables?

Venables Yes, rather. You ought to be on television, sir.

Temple You can catch cold, but you can't catch hot! How fabulous!

Mr Wilkins All right, all right. It wasn't meant to be all that funny.

The laughter subsides

Darbishire Sir, could I have your autograph before the end of term, sir? And I'd like a photo too, if I could.

Mr Wilkins You feeling all right, Darbishire?

Darbishire Just a little sad, that's all. My father says we never appreciate what we've got until it's too late. I wish now I'd worked harder in your lessons, sir.

Mr Wilkins That's quite enough nonsense. Off you go to the bathroom, all of you.

Boys Yes, sir. Certainly, sir.

The Boys, wearing dressing-gowns and slippers and carrying pyjamas, exit along the landing

Mr Wilkins descends the stairs

Mr Carter and the Headmaster enter from the dining-hall, making for the archway

Mr Carter switches on the light

Headmaster . . . but one must make allowances for a boy of that type—sensitive, highly-strung.

Mr Carter Quite.

Headmaster Ah, Wilkins! Have you finished those reports yet?

Mr Wilkins appears not to hear

Wilkins! You seem a little distrait.

Mr Wilkins (*recovering*) Sorry, H.M. It's Dormitory Four. They've gone completely off their heads.

Headmaster Have they been behaving badly?

Mr Wilkins Quite the reverse. They were so polite that it just wasn't true.

Headmaster Really!

Mr Wilkins Well, I ask you: is it natural that a boy like Jennings should feel worried in case I was standing in a draught?

Headmaster H'm!

Mr Wilkins Or that they should want my autograph as though I was a pop singer.

Mr Carter You seem to be very popular all of a sudden.

Mr Wilkins Popular! I was a riot! I made a rather feeble little joke and they all roared their heads off.

Mr Carter What did you say?

Mr Wilkins Oh, it was nothing. I just told Jennings that whether or not I caught cold, he'd catch it hot if he didn't get a move on.

Mr Carter and Headmaster look at him blankly

Mr Carter Well, go on.

Mr Wilkins (*embarrassed*) That was it. That was the joke.

Mr Carter Yes, of course. Very quick of you, Wilkins. I had no idea you had such a ready wit. In fact, I wonder you don't . . . (go on television)

Mr Wilkins All right, all right. You needn't go on about it. I told you it wasn't all that funny. But why should those silly little boys laugh so much?

Mr Carter I'm afraid they were pulling your leg.

Mr Wilkins We'll soon see about that! I shall keep a pretty close eye on those boys, between now and the end of term, and if there are any more disgraceful exhibitions of extremely courteous conduct I'll—I'll—well they'd better look out.

Headmaster Don't take it too much to heart, Wilkins. I'm sure you were just the same forty years ago.

Mr Wilkins I doubt it.

      MUSIC 9. *THE THINGS THEY DO* (reprise)

      It's all so different now from when I was a boy.

      Short trousers and short haircuts were the order of the day.

      We never went around in tee shirts labelled Tottenham

          Hotspur,

      Or let our standards slip in any way.

      They don't carry books in satchels any more

      But plastic bags from Marks and Spencer's store

      You and I had to be able

      To recite our twelve times table.

      They do their sums with calculators, nowadays.

Headmaster Come along, I'm still waiting for those reports.

The Headmaster, Carter and Wilkins exit through the archway, Carter switching off the main hall light. Jennings, Venables, Darbishire and Temple, in dressing-gowns and pyjamas return along landing to the dormitory

Jennings inspects the string on the window-sill as the Boys remove dressing-gowns and get into bed

Jennings It's okay. She'll never notice it there. (*He gets into bed*) All be talking naturally when she comes in, so she won't smell a rat.

Darbishire I can never think of anything to say when I'm trying to sound natural. I—sort of—dry up and go all silent.

Temple That'll make her suspicious for a kick-off.

Darbishire I can't help it. When I've got a guilty secret the words just won't come.

Jennings If you get stuck, just say "rhubarb, rhubarb".

Darbishire Why "rhubarb"?

Jennings It's something actors say to make you think there's a conversation going on. You mutter it, so's no-one can hear.

Darbishire Well, if they can't hear what's the point of . . .

Jennings It's a *pretend* conversation, you clodpoll! Just a sort of buzzing noise for when you can't think of anything to say.

Darbishire Oh, I see. (*He tries it out*) Rhubarb, rhubarb, rhubarb . . .

MUSIC 10.   *RHUBARB*

Jennings   1. Rhubarb, rhubarb, rhubarb, just say rhubarb when
              you're stuck
              Rhubarb, rhubarb, rhubarb, then repeat it just for luck

Darbishire   If you want my opinion it's a crazy thing to say
              Why not: "How's your lumbago" or "The weather's fine
              today"?

Venables   2. Rhubarb, rhubarb, rhubarb, it just doesn't mean a thing
Temple   It's meant to sound like talking or two people arguing.
Jennings   You're only s'posed to mumble it: it's not meant to be heard
              It's just a crazy word.
              It's just a crazy word.

Jennings   3. Suppose you're in a Shakespeare play: you're just one of
              a crowd.
              You haven't any lines to say—at least not out aloud.
              Mark Antony says: "Brutus was an honourable man"
              You can't just stand there silently, you've got to have a
              plan
              So you say:

All   4. Rhubarb, rhubarb, rhubarb, it just doesn't mean a thing
(except   It's meant to sound like talking or two people arguing.
Darbishire)   You're only s'posed to mumble it: it's not meant to be heard
              It's just a crazy word

Darbishire   I see! A crazy word!

Venables   5. You might be imitating Mr Wilkins in a bate

And saying things like: "Doh! You stupid boy, why are
you late?"
When suddenly he marches in to your astonishment.
You've got to keep on talking to put him off the scent
So you say:

All   6. Rhubarb, rhubarb, rhubarb, it just doesn't mean a thing
(except   It's meant to sound like talking or two people arguing.
Darbishire)   You're only s'posed to mumble it: it's not meant to be heard.
It's just a crazy word.
It's just a crazy word.

Temple   7. When Matron comes to put the light out in the dormit'ry
We'll have to keep the conversation flowing naturally
If you run out of dialogue, assume a pious look
And don't forget the magic word that gets you off the hook.
The word is,

All   8. Rhubarb, rhubarb, rhubarb, just say rhubarb when you're
stuck
Rhubarb, rhubarb, rhubarb, then repeat it just for luck.
Perhaps you think it's crazy: you may think it's absurd,
But rhubarb, rhubarb, rhubarb—that's the word.

Matron enters from the landing

Matron You were making enough noise in here! What's going on?
Jennings Nothing, Matron. Nothing really. We were all just chatting
naturally. (*He signals to others to carry on talking*)
Matron Were you, indeed!
Temple (*doing his best*) Er—quite a warm day for the time of year, don't
you think, Venables?
Venables Oh yes. Warmer than yesterday, wouldn't you think?
Temple Much warmer. Warmer than tomorrow too, I shouldn't wonder.

Matron gives them a look

Venables Good night, Matron, good night.
Matron What d'you mean "good night"? I haven't gone yet.
Venables No, but you're just going, aren't you?
Temple And probably warmer than the day after tomorrow. What do you
think, Darbishire?
Darbishire (*at a loss, muttering*) Oh—er—yes—er—rhubarb, rhubarb,
rhubarb.
Matron What did you say, Darbishire?
Darbishire Er—rhubarb, Matron.
Matron Why?
Darbishire No special reason. I just couldn't think of anything else to say.
Matron Are you feeling quite well?
Darbishire Yes, thank you, Matron.
Matron H'm! You're quite right, though. It is warmer tonight. I think
we'll have a little more air in here.

Matron goes to the window. The Boys react in alarm

Jennings (*in a panic*) Oh, Matron!
Matron (*at the window*) Yes?
Jennings Nothing, Matron.

Matron lifts the sash. A faint thud is heard from below. The Boys react in despair

Matron That's funny. I thought I heard something fall. (*She looks out of the window*) Can't see a thing. (*She goes to the door and switches the light off*) Good night, everybody. Sleep well.

Boys (*subdued*) Good night, Matron.

Matron goes out along the landing, leaving the door open

The apparent source of light in the dormitory is from the landing and moonlight through the window. The Boys lie still till Matron is out of earshot, then sit up in bed

Darbishire Coo! Mouldy chizz! Rotten old mouldy chizz!
Jennings Bad luck, Darbi!
Venables It's bad luck for all of us.
Temple Yes, and who was the crazy bazooka who said hang it out of the window?
Venables ⎫ (*hostile*) Jennings! ⎫ *Speaking together*
Temple ⎭   ⎭
Temple Jennings, as usual. It would be.
Venables You might have known it would drop slap-bang-wallop down on to the playground if anyone opened the window.
Temple Crazy scheme! Absolute sabotage!
Jennings You all said what a good idea it was when I suggested it.
Venables If you'd got any decency you'd offer to fox downstairs and get it back.
Jennings No jolly-thank-you. I might meet a master.
Temple Of course you won't. They'll all be busy in the staff room doing reports and stuff.
Jennings It's all very well for you chaps, lying all snug in bed planning dangerous operations for other people to carry out.
Darbishire Hear, hear. After all, what could Jennings say if he *did* meet a master?
Temple He could say . . . (*He has bright idea*) I know! He could say nothing at all. Just go on walking down the stairs without answering— like Lady Macbeth.
Venables Lady Macbeth?
Temple We read it in class with Mr Wilkins.
Venables What about it?
Temple Don't you remember that passage where Lady Macbeth walked in her sleep?
Darbishire It didn't say she walked in a passage. Mr Wilkins said she came down the stairs.
Temple Not that sort of passage, you clodpoll. I mean the scene.

Darbishire Oh, I see. Still, I suppose there *could* have been a passage at the top of the stairs so she could get back to her bedroom afterwards, couldn't there?

Temple That's not the point. The thing is, she was walking in her sleep, so if Jennings *did* meet a master—he won't of course—but if he did, they'd think he was sleep-walking too.

Jennings That's crazy. I'd never get away with it.

Venables Oh, go on, Jen, be decent. It's the only way to get the cake back.

Jennings (*unwillingly*) Oh, all right. I suppose I'll have to. (*He gets out of bed and puts on his dressing-gown and slippers*)

Jennings Come with me, Darbi?

Darbishire (*aghast*) Me! Gosh, no! That'd ruin the whole scheme. You couldn't have *two* Lady Macbeths waltzing down the stairs. It'd look silly.

Jennings So it would if someone saw me marching out of the front door looking for dirty linen bags full of fruit cake. That's not the sort of thing you do in your sleep.

Darbishire No. Well, in that case you could—er—I know. Go and sit down in your desk and get on with your prep.

Jennings You're crazy. I've finished my prep.

Venables gets out of bed, goes to the landing and peers over the banisters

Darbishire But it's just the sort of thing you *would* do if you were walking in your sleep. Your mind's still on your work, you see.

Temple They'll think you've been working too hard and got a brainstorm.

Jennings What, me! Overworking!

Darbishire It's only in case of emergency.

Venables returns to the dormitory

Venables It's all right, Jen. No one about. Go now while the coast's clear. (*He gets back into bed*)

Jennings Oh, all right. It's jolly risky all the same. Lady Macbeth didn't have to worry about running into Old Wilkie. Tt! It's enough to make *anyone* walk in their sleep!

Jennings emerges cautiously on to the landing, looks round and starts descending on tiptoe

When Jennings is half-way down the Headmaster, Mr Carter and Mr Wilkins enter from the archway (staff room), talking amongst themselves

Jennings hears them and stops in panic. He turns to run upstairs again, decides that it is too late to retreat and descends the stairs in sleep-walking trance, with staring eyes and arms held before him. The Masters stop at the bottom of the stairs and regard him with interest. Mr Carter switches on main hall light

Headmaster (*gently*) Jennings! Jennings!

Mr Wilkins What do you think you're playing at boy! Out of bed and chasing about after lights out.

Headmaster Quietly, Wilkins, quietly! (*Gently*) Jennings!

Jennings walks past the Masters and describes a circle round the stage, ending up at the desk. He sits down, opens the desk, takes out a book and studies it with unseeing eyes

Extraordinary!

Mr Wilkins He's just pretending. He's as wide awake as you or I.

Headmaster You may be right. On the other hand, we must avoid precipitate action. It's most dangerous to arouse a sleep-walker.

Mr Wilkins But the boy's awake. So why not tell him to stop being stupid and get back to bed.

Headmaster Let me handle this if you please, Wilkins. (*He moves to Jennings and stands in front of the desk*) Jennings! Jennings! I know quite well you're awake, so stop this play-acting at once . . . Jennings, d'you hear me!

Jennings gives no sign that he has heard. The Headmaster rejoins Mr Carter and Mr Wilkins and leads them down by the piano

This is most disturbing. There's no response at all. He's sitting there reading *Macbeth*—with the book upside down.

Mr Carter The whole situation is topsy-turvy, if I may say so.

Headmaster I'm rather at a loss to know what to do next. If he was one of those ultra-sensitive, highly-strung boys, I should say . . .

Mr Wilkins Jennings! He's about as highly strung as a shrimping net.

Headmaster All the same, I'm beginning to wonder whether my original assumption was correct.

Mr Wilkins You don't mean you think that he really *is* asleep!

Headmaster I don't know what to think. If he *is*, it would be dangerous to waken him suddenly.

Mr Wilkins Yes, but dash it all . . .

Headmaster I think I'll go and have a word with Matron before taking any further action. She's had more experience of this sort of thing; she's bound to know the best psychological approach. Just keep an eye on him, will you!

The Headmaster exits along the landing

Mr Wilkins Well, what do you know about that?

Mr Carter It's stalemate at the moment. He's obviously prepared to go on sitting there . . .

Mr Wilkins But we can't let the silly little boy sit there all night.

Mr Carter He'll sit there until we give him the excuse he needs to get back to his dormitory without awkward explanations.

Mr Wilkins How d'you mean?

Mr Carter Look at it from his point of view. He wants us to believe that he imagines he's still doing his prep. Very well, then. Let's pretend he is. Go and announce that prep's over and it's time for the class to stop

working and go to bed. That'll give him his chance to retire in good
order.

Mr Wilkins You've got something there! Splendid idea. If he's awake he'll
take the hint. If he's asleep—as the Head seems to think—he's bound
to respond to a suggestion like that. Good psychological approach.

Mr Carter Based on observation of the way the youthful mind appears
to work.

Mr Wilkins We'll have him upstairs and between the sheets before the
Head gets back. You see if we don't. (*He is about to go, then turns back*)
You'd better keep well out of the way, Carter. Don't want to scare him
with too many grown-ups looking on.

Mr Carter I'll leave it to you.

Mr Carter exits through the archway (to the staff room)

*Mr Wilkins goes to the corridor, disappears from view and returns imme-
diately as though entering on duty. He is self-conscious about the part he is
playing, and speaks with over-emphasis*

Mr Wilkins H'm. Everybody hard at work? Good! (*He walks between the
imaginary desks affecting to inspect the children's work*) Keep the
writing tidy, Rowena . . . Tt! Look at that smudge, Atkinson. What's
the matter with your pen? . . . Is that all you've done, boy? You've been
wasting your time. You should have got up to Exercise Four by now . . .
Put your hand down, Darbishire. You'll have to wait. (*He stands in
front of the "class" and glances at his watch*) Right! It's time for the end
of prep. Stop working and put your books away, everybody. Quietly
now! Quietly! Come along, Jennings. Time to stop work.

*Still in his "trance", Jennings puts the book in the desk and sits with arms
folded*

That's right . . . Sit still in the front row . . . Don't fidget . . . Now,
I'm going into the corridor to ring the bell for the end of prep. As soon
as the bell goes everybody is to go up to the dormitories and get into
bed. I don't want to find anyone still in here when I get back.

*Mr Wilkins goes to the bell-push, rings the bell for ten seconds, then exits
along the corridor. At the first sound Jennings rises and with arms out-
stretched crosses the room to the foot of the stairs. Then, realizing he is
unobserved, he abandons his trance and dashes out through the archway
to the front door which is heard to slam behind him*

*Simultaneously, when the bell starts the boys in the dormitory sit up and an
excited chatter breaks out in which the words "Fire Drill" are audible. They
sing first verse of song "Fire Drill" as they get out of bed, switch on the
light, close the window and hunt for slippers and dressing-gowns*

MUSIC 11. *FIRE DRILL*

Darbishire	1. Oh gosh what a din for heaven's sake!
Venables	Disturbing me when I'm half awake
Temple	I was just dropping off in my nice warm bed

And now I shall have to get up instead,
Find out the cause of this ghastly noise
Such a strain on the nerves of high-strung boys!
Yes, I know what it is—there's no need to inquire
It's the signal to warn us the building's on fire.

(*Speaking*)   Fire Drill!

At the end of the first verse the Boys put on slippers and dressing-gowns and prepare to leave the room while dialogue proceeds in hall

As the first verse ends, Mr Carter enters from the archway and Mr Wilkins from the corridor. The music of verses two and three, held under, is played during the following dialogue

Mr Carter Was that you ringing the bell?
Mr Wilkins Yes. Rather a neat touch, I thought. End of prep! And it worked splendidly. He's gone upstairs, you see.
Mr Carter Yes, but . . .

The Headmaster, followed by Matron, enters along the landing, and hurries down the stairs in some agitation

Headmaster Wilkins! Was that you ringing the bell?
Mr Wilkins That's right, H.M. All part of the psychological treatment.
Headmaster What on earth possessed you to do such a thing!
Mr Wilkins I was solving your problem for you. Jennings has gone back to bed.
Headmaster Never mind Jennings now. Don't you realize what you've done?
Mr Wilkins (*puzzled*) I beg your pardon?
Headmaster Surely you haven't forgotten that when the bell is rung after lights out it's the signal for fire drill!
Mr Wilkins (*horrified*) Oh my goodness gracious! Yes, of course. Fire practice! I completely forgot!
Headmaster You forgot!
Mr Wilkins In the heat of the moment, you know. It was that boy, Jennings. I was getting him back to bed.
Headmaster Instead of which you've got everybody else out of bed.
Mr Wilkins (*moving to the stairs*) I'll stop them. I'll send them back.
Mr Carter You'll have chaos if you do. The only thing to do now is to have a fire practice as though we'd organized it on purpose. Roll call, inspection of premises—the lot.
Headmaster Infuriating! All right then, Carter, the usual procedure.

The Headmaster exits to the classroom, followed by Mr Wilkins and Matron. Mr Carter exits along the corridor

The Boys file out of the dormitory, singing, and descending the stairs

FIRE DRILL (Cont.)

Darbishire ⎫   2. When once the duty master has put out the light
Venables ⎬   And he's got you into bed—tucked up for the night
Temple   ⎭   A bright idea springs to his puerile brain

To go and ring the bell and get you out again.
But what the poor man simply hasn't realized
Is that he's doing us a great big favour disguised
Because there's nothing that we so much appreciate
As the chance to have some fun and stay up late.

At the end of the second verse Emma, Chris and Rowena, in pyjamas and dressing-gowns, enter along the landing and sing the third verse at the top of the stairs

Emma ⎫ 3. Is it really a fire? Is it only a joke?
Chris ⎬   I can't see any flames. I can't smell any smoke.
Rowena ⎭   We all know what to do. We've been told to keep calm
                 But is it a fire or a false alarm?

Emma, Chris and Rowena descend the stairs and join the Boys for the dance

During the fourth verse all the extra Children, in pyjamas and dressing-gowns, and with the Boys leading, descend the stairs, singing. They line up behind the principal Children for the fifth verse

All   4. A fire drill's just the thing to liven the routine
                In the middle of the night—you know what I mean.
                For life at boarding school is so monotonous
                It's our chance to break the hold Old Wilkie's got on us.
                He cannot say a thing if we should go too far
                And pretend to be more stupid than we really are
                Or make out that we're more sleepy than we can tell
                It's all his fault that trouble's brewing
                It's all Old Wilkie's doing
                It's all his fault because he rang the blinking bell!

All   5. A fire drill's just the thing to liven the routine
                In the middle of the night—you know what I mean.
                For life at boarding school is so monotonous
                It's our chance to break the hold Old Wilkie's got on us.
                He cannot say a thing if we should go too far
                And pretend to be more stupid than we really are
                Or make out that we're more sleepy than we can tell
                It's all his fault that trouble's brewing
                It's all Old Wilkie's doing
                It's all his fault because he rang the bell,
                The blinking bell!

MUSIC 11a.   *FIRE DRILL* (exit)

All exit to the classroom

Through the open door the roll-call can be heard throughout the next action sequence. As the Headmaster reads the names the Children answer "Sir"

As the first name is called, Jennings hurries in from the front door with the linen bag containing Darbishire's cake tin. He runs up to his dormitory

*and hides it beneath his pillow. Then hurries out to the landing and rushes
to the classroom just a little late to answer his name. As Jennings leaves
the dormitory, Mr Carter appears along the landing, notices Jennings'
behaviour and enters the dormitory to investigate*

*He finds the linen bag under the pillow and takes out the cake tin. He is
about to leave when a thought occurs to him. He picks up a pair of shoes
from under a bed and puts them in the linen bag, which he replaces under
Jennings' pillow. He goes down to the hall carrying the cake tin just after
the roll call finishes*

Meanwhile the roll call has been proceeding as follows:

Headmaster (*off*) Archer, Arrowsmith, Atkinson, Barnet, Binns, Blotwell,
Bromwich, Bullard, Callaghan, Cobb, Curran, Darbishire, Davis,
Dodd, Elliot, Fagan, Field, Foster, Gargery, Geldart, Gregory, Hay-
ward, Hemsley, Hibbert, Hill, Isaac, Jennings . . . (*Pause*) Jennings.

Jennings reaches the classroom door and rushes through

Jennings (*off*) Here, sir. Here I am, sir. In person, sir.
Headmaster (*off*) You're late. Report to me afterwards.
Jennings (*off*) Yes, sir.
Headmaster (*off*) Johnson, Kelly, Lewis, Lott, Manning, Martin-Jones,
Matthews, McKay, Mitchell, Neilson, Nuttall, O'Connell, Parslow,
Pettigrew, Pritchard, Richardson, Rumbelow, Saunders, Smith,
Temple, Thompson, Thorpe, Venables, Walker, West, White.

*The Headmaster enters from the classroom, followed by Mr Wilkins and
Jennings*

*Mr Carter comes downstairs. The Headmaster is about to cross when
Jennings speaks*

Jennings Sir, please, sir, you told me to report to you.
Headmaster I did. Why were you late?

Jennings hesitates

Come along, boy, I asked you a question. Why didn't you come down
with the rest of the school when the bell went for fire drill?
Jennings (*puzzled*) Fire drill, sir? (*Light dawns*) Oh, I *see*, sir. I see it all
now. So that *was* the bell for fire drill, after all.
Headmaster What else did you assume it was for?
Jennings Well, I thought I heard someone say it was fire practice, sir,
only I thought it couldn't be because . . . (*He pauses*)
Headmaster Well?
Jennings Because Mr Wilkins had just told me it was the bell for the end
of prep, sir.

Mr Wilkins blows his nose to cover his embarrassment

And you see, sir . . .

Headmaster All right. Upstairs to bed. I don't intend to pursue the matter further at the moment.

MUSIC 11b. FIRE DRILL (reprise)

The Headmaster and Mr Wilkins join Mr Carter

Matron comes in from the classroom and joins them

The "FIRE DRILL" chorus starts again. The staff sing a quartet variation against the Children's chorus, which starts as Darbishire, Venables and Temple enter from the classroom. Jennings joins them and they circle the stage and go up the stairs

All the other Children enter and follow in file

In the dormitory Jennings produces the linen bag and they start a triumphant dance on the beds which ends abruptly as he produces the pair of shoes instead of the cake. Simultaneously, downstairs, Mr Carter exhibits the cake tin to the staff

By this time, the extra Children have gone up the stairs, still singing. As the procession exits along the landing—

the CURTAIN *falls*

MUSIC 12. ENTR'ACTE

ACT II

Scene 1

The same. Early afternoon, two days later

As the CURTAIN *rises, Rowena enters from the dining-hall with a suitcase and some music, hurries to the piano, and starts practising. Two extra Girls enter from the archway and cross to the classroom, carrying suitcases*

Girl What! Doing your practice now! You must be off your runners!
Rowena I'm getting ready for the concert.
Girl Not now, you shouldn't. We've all got to take our things up for packing.
Rowena Tt! It's hopeless. They don't give you a chance.

MUSIC 13. *CROSSING OFF THE DAYS*

All available Children file in, singing, from the corridor carrying empty suitcases on their heads. The column, led by Jennings and joined by Rowena winds round the stage and, after the song, up the stairs. Jennings, Darbishire, Venables and Temple leave their cases by their beds and return downstairs to the hall as the crowd go off along the landing. The singing fades in the distance

All (Chorus) Excuse our breaking out in song,
                Believe you me, it won't last long.
                We'll let off steam and then we'll stop.
                Either that or we'll blow our top.
                For the end of term is drawing near,
                Holidays will soon be here.
                Pack our bags and we'll be off.
                Linbury—good-bye.
                L - I - N - B - U - R - Y
                Good-bye Linbury, 'bye, 'bye, 'bye.

Jennings 1. The term is nearly over, we've been crossing off the days,
            The day after tomorrow we shall go our different ways.
            Seven days, six days, five days, four days, three days,
               two days; one!
            And the holidays will really have begun.

The chorus is repeated after the first, second and third verses. The repeat after the fourth verse is to cover the Children's exit

Chris 2. No more French and Latin; no more English, no more maths,

No more risk of teachers turning into psychopaths
No examinations to confuse my poor old brain
No more risk of going crazy with the strain.

Darbishire 3. Good-bye lumpy mattress in my freezing dormit'ry
Good-bye my school dinners, and good-bye to my school
tea
Bullet-proof potatoes, and bomb-proof hard-boiled eggs
And good-bye to cocoa made from Diesel dregs.

Emma 4. Hurry up, tomorrow; for the next day I shall be
Miles away from boarding-school—miles from Linbury.
Four weeks, three weeks, two weeks, one week, while
we're off the chain.
Then it's back on the treadmill once again.

MUSIC 13a. *EXIT AND MELOS*

As the column goes off along the landing, Jennings, Darbishire, Venables and Temple return downstairs

Jennings Well that's another job done. We'd better get on with that Shakespeare lark now. We've only got till tomorrow to get it ready.
Venables *Henry the Fifth*? We haven't had a chance to learn it yet.
Jennings It's only a short scene: Emma's gone to get the books.
Venables Yes but it's nearly time for afternoon school: and we're giving old Sir his famous farewell gift at the end of the lesson, don't forget.
Jennings Don't worry. That's all taken care of.
Temple You got enough money, then?
Jennings Oh yes. Most chaps gave five p because they were sorry he was leaving; and the rest gave ten p because they were glad.
Temple Cheap at the price, really. What are we giving him?
Jennings You'll see.

Emma enters from the classroom with some textbooks and a trumpet

Emma Here you are, then. Act Four, Scene Three, just before the Battle of Agincourt.

The Boys take the textbooks

Venables What are you doing in it? I thought we weren't having girls.
Emma I'm the prompter. And you'd better watch your step or you won't get a prompt when you dry up.
Jennings *(consulting his book)* Now let's get organized. There's Bedford and Exeter, Salisbury and Gloucester ...
Venables I thought you said we were only doing one scene. That's four different places already.
Darbishire Those aren't places: those are people. If you're a baron you're allowed to call yourself after a county.
Venables Well, you're not a baron, so why do you call yourself Darbishire?

Darbishire Ah, that's different. My father says that many years ago, our family . . .

Jennings All right, let's get on with it. You can be the Duke of Westmorland, Venables: and you're the Duke of Exeter, Temple.

Temple Has it got to be Exeter? Couldn't it be Bournemouth? You see, I went there last holidays and . . .

Jennings No it couldn't. There isn't a Duke of Bournemouth in the play.

Darbishire Bags I be the Duke of Salisbury.

Jennings Okay. We can cut out the Duke of Gloucester because he's only got half a line. I'll be the Duke of Bedford, and there we are.

Emma That's all very well, but you've forgotten Henry the Fifth. You can't cut him out unless you alter the play quite a lot and it's a terribly long part. We'll need someone with a supersonic memory to learn all those speeches by tomorrow.

Temple Well, somebody's got to do it. Who's got a supersonic memory?

Jennings Mr Wilkins!

Incredulous reaction

Venables Fish-hooks, no! Not Old Wilkie! I wouldn't cast him for a character like Henry the Fifth.

Jennings I think he'd be jolly good. He's always telling us how easy it is to learn things by heart, so here's his chance.

Darbishire Yes, you've got something there!

Jennings And we'll keep it a top priority secret, shall we? Then all the audience will think some ordinary chap is going to come on and— wow! Won't they get a surprise!

Emma We'd better ask old Sir first, though.

Jennings I don't mind asking him. Now let's get on with the scene up to where the King comes in.

Emma It starts off with ye royal fanfare off stage. That's my bit. (*She goes to the stairs and blows a fanfare on the trumpet*)

The Boys react

Venables What a ghastly row.

Temple That sounds terrible, Emma.

Emma Well, you come and do better, then. It sounded all right to me, and I ought to know, because I've got a very musical ear, and I'll probably become a famous musician one day, and . . . (perhaps I'll even be asked to play at the . . .)

Jennings All right, all right, get on with it. Don't just stand there blowing your own trumpet.

Emma That's just what I'm supposed to do. How can I sound my famous fanfare if I can't blow my own trumpet?

Jennings Well, *blow* your own trumpet, then, but don't do it so loud. The last blast went in one ear and it hasn't come out of the other yet.

Emma All right. Stand by. (*She blows on the trumpet*)

Mr Wilkins enters from the archway (staff room)

Mr Wilkins What on earth's going on in here! Who was making that
horrible ear-splitting noise?

Emma I was, sir. It was my famous fanfare.

Mr Wilkins It sounded more like stones on a tin roof. If you children
can't amuse yourselves without making all that noise, you won't be
allowed to come in here.

Jennings Oh sir, Mr Wilkins, sir. You're just the person we want, sir.
Will you very kindly do us a favour, sir?

Mr Wilkins It depends what it is.

Jennings Well, you see, sir, we've had to scrap our play about Darbishire's
moustache and we're going to do Shakespeare instead.

Mr Wilkins What's that got to do with me?

Jennings Well, sir, we wondered whether you'd very kindly play Henry
the Fifth for us in the concert tomorrow night. You see, it's too long
for us to learn; and I'm sure you'd be jolly good and the audience
would get a surprise, wouldn't they, sir?

Mr Wilkins Why should they be surprised if I'm good?

Jennings Oh, I didn't mean that, sir.

Mr Wilkins I should hope not indeed.

Emma Still, if it's too difficult for you, sir . . .

Mr Wilkins Too difficult! Don't be ridiculous. I could play a part like
that on my head, if I wanted to.

Emma We wouldn't want to surprise the audience all that much, sir! If
you'd just play it the right way up, that'd be good enough for us. Here's
where it starts, sir. Top of the page. (*She gives a book to Mr Wilkins*)

Mr Wilkins Yes, I see. All right; how's this?

"What's he that wishes so?
My cousin Westmoreland? No, my fair cousin:
If we are mark'd to die, we are enow
To do our country loss; and if to live,
The fewer men, the greater share of honour."

Jennings	Oh, jolly good, sir!
Darbishire	Fabulous! Fantastic!
Temple	Wow, sir! I never knew you were such a jolly good actor, sir!
Venables	You ought to be on television, sir!
Emma	As good as Laurence Olivier—easily!

(*Speaking together*)

Mr Wilkins H'm. I suppose it wasn't too bad for a first effort. All right,
I'll play King Henry for you. But you'll have to rehearse without me;
I shan't have time for that. I'll have a look at the part some time this
evening. I don't suppose it'll take me more than a few minutes to learn.

Emma Won't it really, sir? Not many people could learn all that in a few
minutes. You must have got a computerized think-tank, sir.

Mr Wilkins It's quite easy, if you put your mind to it.

Jennings And you won't tell anyone, will you? We want it to be a surprise.

Mr Wilkins Yes, well never mind about that. Just at the moment I've
got a lot of reports to write, and I can't do it with you people raising Cain

outside the staff room. Go and find somewhere else to do your rehearsing.

Boys Yes sir.

Emma Come on, let's go to the gym.

The Children start to go

Mr Wilkins And another thing . . .

The Children stop

Matron wants everybody's football and hockey boots cleaned and ready for packing before afternoon school.

Darbishire Please sir, I've lost my football boots, sir.

Mr Wilkins (*with patient resignation*) Go and *look* for them, then!

Darbishire Yes sir.

The Children, except Jennings, exit to the corridor

Jennings And thank you ever so much for being Henry the Fifth, sir. (*Laying it on*) I'm sure you'll be ever so good, sir: just like a real, professional actor.

Mr Wilkins (*pleased*) You think so! We shall have to see, shan't we.

Jennings exits to the corridor

Mr Wilkins adopts a dramatic pose and reads from his book

"What's he that wishes so?
My cousin Westmoreland? No, my fair cousin:
If we are mark'd to die, we are enow
To do our country loss; and if to live,
The fewer men, the greater share of honour."

MUSIC 14. *I CAN SEE MYSELF*

Mr Wilkins 1. I can see myself in this stirring royal role
    A Lancastrian King, striving heart and soul
    To make good his oath in the eyes of the world.

2. I can see myself as a king in days of yore
    Astride my horse on the field of Agincourt
    With my head held high, and my flag unfurled.

3. I can see myself declaiming on the stage
    Defending a righteous cause.
    The audience held in the hollow of my hand
    Till they break into rapt applause.

4. If only I'd chosen a career upon the stage
    A famous actor I might be
    But it's too late now—I know my fate, now.
    My job is teaching Form Three.

5. I espoused the Thespian muse—or does that sound
        high-falutin'?
    But an unkind Fate—intervened and put the boot in.
    If only I had sailed—on a different course.

6. I might have played the lead at Stratford for a season
   Playing all the parts that came my way—well, all parts
       within reason
   For I'd draw the line—at a pantomime horse.

7. I can see my Hamlet praised by the *Guardian* and
       The Times.
   My Othello—a "must" for all to see.
   My King Lear would be hailed as the triumph of the age
   My Macbeth would top the ratings on T.V.

8. But it's all a dream I shall never realize
   A "might-have-been" fantasy
   The bubble's burst, now—I know the worst, now
   All my life I'll be stuck with Form Three.

Mr Wilkins consults the book and rehearses the first line with varying modulations

(*Bass*) "What's he that wishes so? My cousin Westmoreland?" H'm. Too old. (*Treble*) "What's he that wishes so? My cousin Westmoreland?" Mustn't overdo it.

Mr Carter enters from the corridor

"What's he that wishes so?"
Mr Carter What's who that wishes what?
Mr Wilkins Oh—er—nothing Carter; nothing at all really. D'you want me?
Mr Carter The Headmaster does. He's waiting for your reports.

Rowena enters from the dining-hall. Unobserved, she sits at the piano and sorts out music

Mr Wilkins All right, all right, no need to panic. I'm doing them now. I'll see he gets them before afternoon school.
Mr Carter I'll tell him.

Mr Carter exits to the classroom

Mr Wilkins consults the book and mouths the lines silently with gestures

Mr Wilkins (*inaudibly*) "What's he that wishes so?
               My cousin Westmoreland? No, my fair cousin:
               If we are mark'd to die, we are enow
               To do our country loss; and if to live,
               The fewer men . . ."

Rowena starts practising. Mr Wilkins wheels round in exasperation

Oh, for goodness sake, girl! Must you?

Rowena stops playing

Rowena Don't you like music, then, sir?

Mr Wilkins Not that sort, no!

Rowena Shall I play you something else, then? (*She flicks through the music book*) How about *The Merry Peasant*, sir? It's ever so jolly!

Mr Wilkins (*starting softly and working up to a roaring crescendo*) Tt! Listen, my child. I'm going into the staff room to write some very important reports; and I'm not going to have my eardrums shattered by merry jolly peasants thumping and crashing on the other side of the door. (*He goes to the archway*)

Rowena dissolves in tears. Mr Wilkins turns and sees her

Oh dear! Look, I'm sorry, I didn't mean to—er—all I meant was—just keep it quiet.

Mr Wilkins exits through the archway

Rowena (*turning back to the piano*) Ever so quiet! Piano! Pianissimo! Soft pedal hard down! (*She starts playing her song, then leaves the piano and comes down stage as the orchestra takes over*)

MUSIC 15. UNMUSICAL MOB

1. C D E F G, F E D C: C G E
   D E F G A, G F E D: D A F
   Got to get it right
   Before tomorrow night
   If only they'll give me a chance and not keep interfering.

2. Why won't they let me practise?
   What have they got against me?
   Between you and me the fact is
   They're riddled with jealousy
   Riddled with jealous—
   Green with envious—
   Yellow-eyed jealousy.

3. It's no use my pretending I'm a virtu-oso
   Surely you can listen—it won't hurt you: oh, so
   Many times each day
   I settle down to play
   But every time I get this far, someone comes in and—
   (*Speaking*)   Yaketty, yaketty, yak—it's hopeless!

4. Why won't they let me practise?
   What have they got against me?
   Between you and me the fact is
   They're riddled with jealousy
   Riddled with jealous—
   Green with envious—
   Yellow-eyed jealousy.

5. Let's say I'm going to play a Polonaise by Chopin
   I can play it with my eyes shut or my eyes wide open
   But just as I begin
   Old Wilkie marches in
   And says (*speaking*) "You can't play now, my girl; we
      need this room for table tennis."

6. Why won't they let me practise?
   What have they got against me?
   Between you and me the fact is
   They're riddled with jealousy.
   Riddled with jealous—
   Green with envious—
   Yellow-eyed jealousy.

7. I might be playing Mozart or a piece by Purcell
   All I want is half an hour for a rehearsal.
   What a hope I've got!
   Some wretched little clot
   Is bound to come and say (*speaking*) "Rowena! Matron
   wants you in the wash-room."

8. Why won't they let me practise?
   Let me get on with the job?
   Between you and me the fact is
   They're just an unmusical mob.
   Just an unmusical,
   Perishing, thick-headed,
   Cretinous, Philistine mob!

Rowena sits at the piano and resumes her practice. After a few notes she breaks off as the Boys are heard approaching noisily

(*To the audience*) See what I mean!

Jennings enters from the corridor carrying an alarm clock in a box and followed by Darbishire, Venables, Temple, Chris and Emma

Jennings Gather round, everybody. Last chance to see Mr Wilkins' famous farewell gift before it's handed over.

Jennings produces the clock. Delighted reaction from all

Venables An alarm clock. Super!
Emma Just the thing to wake him up at his new school.
Jennings It's got a fabulous bell. Listen!

He sets the bell ringing for some seconds, then switches it off and resets it

We'll hide it till the end of the lesson, then I'll hand it over. (*He replaces the clock in the box and hides it behind the piano*)

Chris Someone ought to make a speech to go with it. You can't just bung it at him and say, "Here you are."

Darbishire Bags I make the speech. I could say—er—(*He strikes pompous attitude*)—Mr Wilkins, Ladies and Gentlemen. Unaccustomed as I am to public speaking, it gives me great pleasure to come here this afternoon, on this histrionic occasion and say . . .

Temple Rhubarb, rhubarb, rhubarb, rhubarb, rhubarb.

An extra Boy enters from the corridor, consults his watch and presses the bell-push, continuing it for some seconds

Venables Bell for school. Back to the salt mines!

MUSIC 16. *FAMOUS FIRST WORDS* (backing)

The Form Three Children enter

There is general activity as they pull the desks down stage C and place them sideways to the audience. (NOTE: *The desks can be pre-set, or brought on by the Children*)

Other Children enter, chatting, from various entrances, some of them crossing and going out through the classroom door. Rowena is amongst them

The Children with the desks sit in their places, facing one of the walls

Mr Carter enters from the classroom, crosses to the archway and exits to the staff room, reappears with a pile of books and exits again to the classroom. The Headmaster enters down the stairs and exits to the dining-hall

The music stops. The Children of Form Three are seated in the desks, with Jennings and Darbishire together in the back row and down stage. Rowena's desk is empty. The class comprises twelve or more children

Jennings Hey, listen, everyone! Not a word to Sir about his leaving present until the end of the lesson. He mustn't even suspect.

Children Righto—Of course not—What do you take us for?

Darbishire Better make sure of my speech. "Mr Wilkins and Gents. Unaccustomed as I am to public speaking . . ." No, wait a sec. I could say, "On this historic occasion . . ."

There is a buzz of conversation amongst the class

Mr Wilkins, carrying a book, enters from the archway

Venables Look out! He's coming!

Conversation stops abruptly, except for Darbishire concentrating on his speech

Darbishire "Unaccustomed as I am to public speaking, it gives me . . . (great pleasure)"

Children Good afternoon, sir.

Mr Wilkins (*moving down and turning to face the class*) 'Afternoon! It's gone very quiet in here all of a sudden—except for Darbishire. What were you saying just then?

Darbishire (*embarrassed*) I was saying, "unaccustomed as I was", sir.

Mr Wilkins Unaccustomed as you were to what?

Darbishire Nothing really sir. I'm accustomed to all sorts of things, actually.

Mr Wilkins Well *I* am unaccustomed to having silly little boys trying to be funny in my class. Any nonsense from this form during this lesson and I'll . . . Well, I'm warning you . . . Now, open your poetry books at page nineteen.

Buzz and chatter as class get their books from the desks

Quietly, there—*quietly*!

Venables Sir, which page sir?

Mr Wilkins Page nineteen.

Chris Page nineteen, sir?

Mr Wilkins You heard what I said.

Chris I just wanted to make sure, sir.

Mr Wilkins Right! Everybody got the place?

Temple Sir, which page did you say?

Mr Wilkins Tt! Why don't you listen! I've told you the page four times already.

Emma Page four, sir? I thought you said page nineteen just now.

Mr Wilkins This class is the limit. I've just told you—page four the nineteenth time—I mean, page nineteen for the fourth time.

Venables That's the fifth time, sir.

Mr Wilkins Right. Now we're going to study part of a poem by Alfred, Lord Tennyson, so all sit up straight and keep your wits sharpened because I shall be asking you questions about it. Now listen carefully. (*Reading*)

"Ring out wild bells to the wild sky
The flying cloud, the frosty light . . ."
(The year is dying in the night)

Chris puts up her hand, waving to attract attention as Mr Wilkins starts reading

Chris Sir, please, sir! Sir, please, sir. Sir!

Mr Wilkins (*irritated*) What is it? I will not be interrupted while I'm reading.

Chris Sorry, sir. I only wondered, shall we have to write the questions in our books, sir?

Mr Wilkins Of course you'll have to write them in your books you silly little girl. You don't imagine I want them embroidered on the lamp shade, do you?

Chris No, sir.

Mr Wilkins Now, no more silly questions. "Ring Out Wild Bells", by Alfred, Lord Tennyson.

Emma has a spasm of coughing

"Ring out wild . . ." Will you stop that horrible noise, Emma!
Emma Sorry, sir! It's my cough, sir. Matron's very kindly giving me . . .
(some medicine for it)
Mr Wilkins All right, all right. Only keep it quiet while I'm reading.
Emma Yes, sir.
Mr Wilkins "Ring Out Wild Bells."
"Ring out wild bells to the wild sky"

There is a knock on the classroom door

"The flying cloud, the frosty light . . ."

The knock is repeated

(*Loudly*) Come in!

Pause. The knock is repeated

(*Shouting*) Oh for goodness sake! Don't stand out there beating on the panels like a panel beater! Come in, if you must.

The door opens. Rowena enters

Rowena Sorry I'm late, sir. I was putting my music away.
Mr Wilkins You should have been here five minutes ago.
Rowena Why, what happened? Did I miss something?
Mr Wilkins Doh! (*He waves Rowena away to her desk*) This is the fourth time I've tried to recite this poem without getting beyond the first verse; and I've had enough of it. One more sound from this class . . . (*He pauses—there is dead silence*) Now, we'll start again. H'm. "Ring Out Wild Bells", by Alfred, Lord Tennyson. "Ring out wild bells . . ."

There is a loud, shrill ringing of the alarm clock from behind the piano. It continues during the sequence

I—I—I . . . Doh! Who's ringing out that wild bell! I mean, where's that noise coming from?
Jennings I'm terribly sorry, sir. It must have gone off by accident.
Mr Wilkins Don't stand there talking. Stop it ringing, at once!

Jennings goes to the piano and has difficulty removing the clock from the box. By the time he succeeds Mr Wilkins is fuming with exasperation. Jennings removes the clock and stops the alarm

Did you put that wretched alarm clock in there?
Jennings (*subdued*) Yes, sir. It was a special secret surprise that we'd planned for you, sir.
Mr Wilkins How dare you plan secret surprises to let off wild alarm bells in the middle of my lesson!
Jennings No, sir; you don't understand, sir.
Mr Wilkins Oh yes, I do understand. The impudence! The insolence! The impertinence! I shall deal with this form after school. Meanwhile . . . (*He holds out his hand for the clock*)
Jennings (*distressed*) Oh *no*, sir! You can't confiscate it. I mean you can't have it till the end of the lesson, because . . . (*He catches sight of*

Mr Wilkins' expression and hands over the clock)

Darbishire ⎱
Venables ⎰ But sir, you don't understand. ⎱*Speaking together*
Mr Wilkins Quiet!

Reaction from the class

Temple ⎱ Oh no, sir. You've gone and spoilt it all. ⎱
Emma ⎰ But sir, it's not fair. Jolly well not fair. ⎰ *Speaking*
Chris ⎱ You can't confiscate it, sir. ⎱ *together*
Rowena ⎰ It was just an accident, honestly it was. ⎰
Mr Wilkins Quiet! Quiet! Appalling behaviour. I will not tolerate such disgraceful conduct.

The class reaction rises to an uproar. The alarm clock goes off in Mr Wilkins' pocket. He leaps as though stung and struggles to get it out

The dining-hall door opens. The Headmaster is standing on the threshold, holding a file of reports

The uproar subsides: the alarm clock stops ringing. Dead silence

Headmaster Well really, Mr Wilkins, it may be the end of term, but that is hardly sufficient reason for allowing your lesson to degenerate into—ah—well, be that as it may, I should like a word with you if you can spare me a moment.
Mr Wilkins (*flustered*) Yes, of course, H.M. of course.
Headmaster Your reports on Form Three's work in English: there are one or two queries—perhaps you'd come along to my study.
Mr Wilkins Of course, of course. (*To the class*) Carry on reading your poetry books till I get back.

The Headmaster and Mr Wilkins exit to the dining-hall

Venables Mouldy chizz! Rotten old mouldy chizz. And it was all Jennings' fault. If he hadn't let the clock go off while Sir was woffling about wild bells everything would have been all right.
Emma You can't blame Jennings. How was he to know what old Sir was going to woffle about.
Rowena What makes it worse is that he doesn't even know it's his own clock that he's confiscated.
Darbishire And then there's my speech, too. Absolutely ruined. I was going to say how happy I was and what pleasure it gave me on this important occasion . . .
Temple Well it wouldn't have given us any pleasure. The only decent thing about the whole business is that we didn't have to sit here listening to you woffling your head off about how happy you were.
Chris It's no good accusing each other. It's all old Wilkie's fault. He's jolly well not fair.
Jennings Hear hear! Three boos for sir.

MUSIC 17. *THREE BOOS FOR SIR* (reprise)

The class now stands. Jennings "conducts" the singing from the front. The last verse (eight) only is required. This may be preceded by verse seven if desired

All   Three boos for Sir!
                 The trouble with teachers when they teach
                 Three boos for Sir!
                 They never practise what they preach,
                 They say: Take our advice, boys,
                 Be quiet as little mice, boys,
                 Eat up your prunes and rice, boys,
                 It's really rather nice, boys.
                 But whatever you do, whatever you do,
                 You're sure to be wrong if you do as they do.
                 Never do as they do,
                 Always do as they say,
                 And keep out of their way!

                                     CURTAIN

MUSIC 18. *SCENE CHANGE* leading to MUSIC 19

                                     SCENE 2

The same. Evening, the following day

The classroom furniture has been cleared. Rowena's music is on the piano As the CURTAIN *rises, Jennings, Darbishire, Venables and Temple are rehearsing for the concert. Emma is prompting*

MUSIC 19. *I CAN SEE MYSELF* (backing, pianissimo)

Darbishire "God's arm strike with us! 'tis a fearful odds.
                 God be wi' you, princes all; I'll to my charge:
                 If we no more meet till we meet in heaven,
                 Then joyfully my"—er—whatever your name is.
                 (*He moves to Temple*)
Emma "My noble Lord of Bedford"—and that's Jennings, not Temple.
Darbishire Okay, okay. (*He moves to Jennings*)
Emma Well get it right, for goodness sake. We shan't have time for any
        more rehearsals.
Darbishire "Then joyfully, my noble Lord of Bedford
                 My dear Lord Gloucester . . ." Hey, where is he?
Emma We've cut out the Duke of Gloucester.
Darbishire Oh! "—and my good Lord Exeter (*He moves to Temple*)
                 And my kind kinsman, warriors all, adieu!"
Jennings "Farewell, good Salisbury; and good luck go with thee!"

Pause

Emma Wake up, Temple, it's you.
Temple Oh, sorry. "Farewell, kind Lord. Fight valiantly today:
    And yet I do thee wrong to mind thee of it,
    For thou art fram'd of the firm truth of valour."
Darbishire Exit Lord Salisbury! (*He retires to the staircase*)
Jennings "He is as full of valour as of kindness;
    Princely in both."

Rowena enters from the dining-hall, goes to the piano and studies her music in silent rehearsal

Venables "O! that we now had here
    But one ten thousand of those men in England
    That do no work today."

Pause. The music fades out

Temple Well, go on, somebody. Who is it, Emma?
Emma This is where Henry the Fifth comes on. We'll have to do without him for now. Old Wilkie said he was too busy to come.
Venables This is hopeless.
Emma It'll be all right. He promised to learn it. He said so.
Venables Yes, but all the same . . .

Mr Carter enters from the archway carrying a handful of letters

Mr Carter Come along, you people. It's too late now for any more rehearsals.
Emma We've had to stop anyway, sir. We can't get any further without Mr Wilkins.
Mr Carter *He's* not in the cast, is he?
Emma Yes sir. Didn't you know? He's Henry the Fifth.
Mr Carter Should be interesting.
Jennings I wish now we'd never asked him.
Emma It'll be all right, Jennings. He promised faithfully.
Jennings It's not only that. Who wants to be in a play with Mr Wilkins after what happened yesterday!

Chris enters along the landing with swords, helmets etc. She puts these properties on a bed in the dormitory and comes downstairs

Chris and Rowena react to the dialogue from the rest of the group

Mr Carter I beg your pardon!
Jennings Well it's true, sir. Something terrible happened, and it's most unfair and it's all Mr Wilkins' fault.
Mr Carter Oh?
Darbishire Yes sir, you see Jennings collected five p from everyone in the form to buy him a clock.
Mr Carter Very generous of Jennings—but why?
Jennings We thought he'd like it sir. And we were going to give it to him at the end of the lesson but the alarm went off in the middle and he confiscated it.

Emma So how can we give him his present when he's got it already but doesn't know.

Mr Carter He must know he's got it!

Jennings But he doesn't know it's his own farewell gift, sir. You see when we heard that he was leaving . . .

Mr Carter Leaving! What makes you think Mr Wilkins is leaving?

Jennings I heard the Head tell you, sir. He said: "Mr Wilkins is leaving this term."

Mr Carter So he is. But he's coming back again next term.

Reaction

He's merely leaving by an earlier train than anyone else.

Emma Oh no!

Temple Coo! I want my five p back.

All (*in a derisive chorus*) Jen—nings!

Jennings Terribly sorry. You see I thought . . .

Rowena Never mind what you thought. You've spent all our money and Sir's got the clock under false pretences.

Mr Carter H'm! I think I'd better see Mr Wilkins for you and explain the little misunderstanding.

Jennings Would you really? Thanks ever so much, sir.

Chris Yes, but even if he *does* give it back, what are we going to do with it?

Mr Carter That'll need thinking out, won't it. (*He hands the letters to Jennings*) Would you like to give these out for me.

Jennings Yes sir.

Mr Carter exits along the corridor

Jennings flicks through the envelopes

They're all for Matron. One, two, three, four—wow! Matron's got nine letters, all by the same post.

Rowena They're birthday cards. You can tell by the shape.

Jennings Matron's birthday. Yippee! Now I know what we can do with the clock.

Darbishire Fancy Matron having a birthday! You'd never think it to look at her, would you.

MUSIC 20. *I NEVER KNEW MATRONS HAD BIRTHDAYS*

Darbishire 1. I never knew Matrons had birthdays
        It's not the sort of thing that you'd expect.
        Do you think that it's really her birthday,
        Or is she saying so, just for effect?

Jennings   It's the chance we need to do a noble deed
        Present her with a present with the minimum fuss.

Darbishire   If Matrons really have birthdays,
        They must be human beings like us.

Girls 2. As the term drags by, Matron grows wearier
Of making boys and girls do what they're told.
But under her stern-faced exterior
Perhaps there beats a heart of purest gold.
Yet when you see her in the dormit'ry,
You never see much sign of any tender hearts
She tells you off in no uncertain terms,
And never stops when once she starts.

All 3. Now scrub your knees and brush your hair,
Change your pants and pull up your socks.
And clean your teeth and pick up that chair,
Put your garters on.
Tuck in your shirt and make yourself smart
Straighten your tie and wash your face.
Then put your sponge-bag back on the shelf,
You look such a disgrace.

Girls 4. She spends so much time giving orders,
A restful break is what she deserves.
For twelve weeks of coping with boarders
Has clearly had an effect upon her nerves.
Perhaps the strain has slightly deranged her brain,
A fact that we must do our best to comprehend
We'll treat her with sweet loving kindness
To stop her going round the bend.

During the following verse the Children mime the various actions

All 5. Now scrub our knees and brush our hair,
Change our pants and pull up our socks.
And clean our teeth and pick up that chair,
Put our garters on.
Tuck in our shirt and make ourselves smart
Straighten our tie and wash our face.
Then put our sponge-bag back on the shelf,
We look such a disgrace.

Darbishire 6. I never knew Matrons had birthdays,
The thought to me—had not occurred.

Rowena But now that we know it's her birthday
To ignore the fact would be absurd.

All So let's organize a genuine surprise
Enrol some volunteers to get the whole scene set,
For, now that we know it's her birthday,
Let's make it a day she won't forget.

Matron enters along the landing, carrying an armful of home-made "Henry V" costumes, which she puts on a bed in the dormitory and then comes to the head of the stairs, after switching on the light

Matron Come along, Jennings, and you others if you want your costumes. It's nearly time for the concert.

Jennings Costumes! Jolly good! Come on, then.

Jennings, Darbishire, Venables and Temple move to the stairs

(*Whispers*) And don't say anything to her about you-know-what.

Mr Carter enters along the corridor and rings the electric bell, holding it for some seconds

Rowena Bell for concert! Oh my goodness, I've got butterflies. Where's my music? (*She takes her music and exits to the classroom*)

Emma And where's my book? They'll never manage without a prompter.

MUSIC 20a.   *MELOS*

All available Extras, some carrying musical instruments, come on from various entrances. With Emma and Chris they cross the stage and exit through the door to the dining-hall

In the dormitory, Matron takes her birthday cards and gives out costumes to Jennings, Darbishire, Venables and Temple who put them on

The Headmaster enters through the archway

The music fades

Headmaster Ah, Carter! Everything under control?

Mr Carter Yes, I think so.

Headmaster No sign of our—ah——guest artist yet?

Mr Carter Uh? Oh, Irving Borrowmore. He *is* coming then?

Headmaster I can only hope so. There was some doubt when I rang up about his being able to get here in time, but he's promised to do his best.

Mr Carter I'll keep a look-out for him.

Headmaster Splendid. I'd better go ahead and get things organized.

Mr Carter exits down the corridor and the Headmaster to the dining-hall

In the dormitory, Matron is helping boys with their costumes—cloaks, helmets, swords, etc. Jennings has a breast-plate and leg guards

Matron No, you're putting it on upside down. There, that's better.

Darbishire Wow! Look at my armour-plated helmet. Do I look like the Earl of Salisbury, Matron?

Matron I couldn't have told you apart, Darbishire.

Temple Won't the audience get a surprise when Henry the Fifth comes on? Of course *you* know who it is, don't you, Matron?

Matron I've no idea.

Temple But you *must* know, Matron, because—what about his costume?

Matron I hope he's quite small, whoever it is. There's only this left. (*She holds up the costume*)

Venables Oh, *Matron*! Mr Wilkins will never be able to get into a titchy little tunic like that!

Matron Mr Wilkins! Surely he's not playing King Henry?

Temple Yes, Matron. Didn't Jennings tell you?

Matron This is the first I've heard of it. There's nothing here that would fit a grown-up the size of Mr Wilkins. Why didn't you say so before, Jennings?

Jennings I'm terribly sorry, Matron. It was a secret, you see.

Temple You've ruined the whole show, Jennings. You can't have Henry the Fifth coming on in a tatty old tweed jacket and baggy trousers. What'll people think?

Jennings We'll just have to think of something else for him to wear, that's all.

Venables (*in panic*) But there's no time. The audience are going in!

Jennings Oh, gosh! Well, I wonder if he'd mind wearing this. He could sort of drape it round his shoulders. (*He takes a red blanket from his bed*)

Venables Don't be crazy. He'd look like a Red Indian Chief!

Jennings Well, it's better than nothing. And for a helmet he could wear —well, he could wear . . .

Temple Well, what? There just isn't anything.

Jennings Yes, there is. There's a brass coal-scuttle in the lumber room.

Darbishire But it's not even clean. Tt! Here's the whole school ready and waiting for a super Shakespeare production, and Henry the Fifth comes on in a red blanket and a coal-scuttle.

Venables You great clodpoll, Jennings. You've messed up the whole operation from blast-off to splash-down. And after Mr Wilkins has learnt his part specially on purpose, too!

Jennings Well, it's too late to do anything about it now. You chaps get ready, and I'll go and get Mr Wilkins his coal-scuttle. Gosh, I hope it fits him.

Jennings and Matron exit along the landing. The others go downstairs and exit to the dining-hall. Mr Carter enters from the corridor and Mr Wilkins from the archway (staff room) with a file of reports

Mr Carter Hullo, Wilkins. Ready for the concert?

Mr Wilkins I wish I was, Carter! But—well I just don't know what to do.

Mr Carter Oh?

Mr Wilkins You see, I rashly agreed to play Henry the Fifth when the boys asked me yesterday afternoon.

Mr Carter Splendid, Wilkins! Mind you're good! We shall expect an outstanding performance.

Mr Wilkins Yes, yes, yes, but what I'm trying to tell you is that I don't know the part.

Mr Carter No?

Mr Wilkins Not more than the first few lines, anyway. I've been so busy with these wretched reports that I haven't had time to learn it.

Mr Carter It's a bit late in the day to say that now. You're due on the stage in about ten minutes.

Mr Wilkins (*in a panic*) I can't go on! It's impossible. There's about

fifty lines in the first speech and all I know is the first three. Tt! How do
they go? Er—
    "What's he that wishes so? My cousin What's—it—er—
    My cousin Westmoreland? No, my fair cousin,
    If we are—er—if we are something-or-other,
    We are enow to—er—to—er . . ."
Oh, it's hopeless, Carter. I just don't know it at all. I wish I could think
of a way to get out of it.

Mr Carter You can't back out, now. The show must go on. Oh, and I
want a word with you about that alarm clock . . .

Mr Wilkins Oh, for goodness sake! I've got *real* problems.

Mr Carter Later, then (*starting to go*), and best of luck for the performance.

*Mr Carter exits to the dining-hall. Jennings appears on the landing with
the red blanket and a coal-scuttle and comes downstairs*

Jennings Sir, Mr Wilkins, sir.

Mr Wilkins What is it, Jennings?

Jennings Well, sir, I'm terribly sorry, but we've made a bit of a bish about
your costume, sir, and . . .

Mr Wilkins Costume! You don't mean you're expecting me to *dress up*
for this ghastly charade, do you?

Jennings Yes, of course, sir. We all are. But the only thing I can find for
you is this blanket and this coal-scuttle and . . .

Mr Wilkins I—I—! I'm not wearing that and don't you think it!

Jennings Oh, please, sir. We're all ready to start.

Mr Wilkins I never heard such ridiculous nonsense in my life! No,
Jennings, I positively refuse to march on to the stage in front of the
whole school wearing a dirty brass scuttle, smothered in coal dust. It's
all off, you understand. I am *not* going to perform.

Jennings Oh, but, sir, please! And after you've taken all the trouble to
learn your part.

Mr Wilkins I—I . . . You heard what I said, Jennings. I suggest you go
and ask the Headmaster to announce that the item's been cancelled.
And that's my last word.

Mr Wilkins exits to the dining-hall

*The concert starts, off, with the choir singing the first bars of the School
Song (recorded). The dining-hall door is supposedly sound-proof, and the
concert is audible only when this door is open. The door shuts on Mr Wilkins.
Jennings stands staring after him, then turns and moves away*

*Irving Borrowmore, in an overcoat and carrying a suitcase, enters from
the archway (front door)*

Jennings Oh gosh, what on earth can I do!

Borrowmore (*coming down*) What can you do, young man? Well for a
start you can tell me where I'm supposed to get ready for my performance.

Jennings (*turning*) Oh! You made me jump. Er—who are you?

Borrowmore Who am I! Does the name Irving Borrowmore convey anything to you?

Jennings No. Not a thing.

Borrowmore Pity! I had hoped that my reputation would have preceded me; but no matter. Tell me, why do you wear a cardboard chest-protector and plastic shin-pads? A new fashion?

Jennings No, it's my armour plating.

Borrowmore Ah yes. A useful precaution when paying a visit to the Headmaster's study. I remember when I was at school . . .

Jennings No, it's nothing like that. I'm wearing my armour because we were going to do a chunk out of Henry the Fifth, but now Mr Wilkins has spoilt it all and won't go on—just because he's only got a coal-scuttle for a helmet.

Borrowmore And is that serious?

Jennings Serious! Of course it's serious. The audience are all sitting there and the cast are all ready and Matron's made us these costumes and—well—what's going to happen now?

Borrowmore H'm! Which part of the play were you hoping to perform?

Jennings Only a short bit; that scene before the battle of Agincourt where he comes on and talks about the feast of Crispian—if you know the bit I mean.

Borrowmore I do, indeed.

> "This day is called the feast of Crispian,
> He that outlives this day, and comes safe home,
> Will stand a-tip-toe when this day is named,
> And rouse him at the name of Crispian.
> He that shall live this day and see old age
> Will yearly on the vigil feast his neighbours,
> And say 'Tomorrow is Saint Crispian . . .' "

Jennings Wow! Why, you're even better than Mr Wilkins. Fancy you knowing all that speech off by heart.

Borrowmore Hardly surprising, dear boy, considering that I've come here specially to recite it. It forms one of the items of my repertoire.

Jennings Does it! I say, would you be awfully decent and go on and do it now, in our play? Everything's all ready, and here's the coal-scuttle and the red blanket. They're not much to look at, but . . .

Borrowmore I don't somehow see myself in this. (*He rejects the coal-scuttle*) Fortunately, I have something a little more suitable in my bag.

(*He opens his case*)

Jennings Wow! Real armour! I say, sir, it'd be fabulous if you'd really play King Henry for us. Will you?

Borrowmore It's all wrong of course. Me, playing with amateurs—and pretty young ones at that. Unthinkable, really! What would Equity say! Still, I see your problem, young man. The show must go on. Fair enough, then. Take me to my dressing-room! Give me time to get ready, then let the curtain rise on Agincourt!

Jennings Oh thank you, sir. Thank you ever so.

Matron enters along the landing and descends the stairs as though en route for the dining-hall

Oh, Matron! May Henry the Fifth change in our dorm, please?
Matron Henry . . . ? But I thought Mr Wilkins was acting for you.
Jennings Change of cast, Matron. I'm putting on an understudy.
Matron I see. You'd better come with me Mr—er . . .
Borrowmore Irving Borrowmore, Matron.
Matron Yes of course—the actor. I remember seeing you in—what was it now?
Borrowmore (*delighted*) *Hamlet*, perhaps? Or was it *Richard III*?
Matron I don't think so.
Borrowmore It could have been *Peer Gynt*. Or perhaps as the Archbishop in *Murder in the.* . . . (*Cathedral*)
Matron No, I've got it! Krunchie-Wunchie Cat Food. You're the man who serves out the cat's meat in the T.V. commercial.
Borrowmore I—er—perhaps you'll show me to my dressing-room.
Matron Of course. This way, Mr Borrowmore.

Matron leads the way upstairs and exits along the landing, followed by Borrowmore

Rowena, with her music, enters from the classroom, goes to the dining-hall, opens the door, and reacts to the singing. The singing stops as she closes the door

Rowena Oh golly, they've started. I'm on in a few minutes.
Jennings Well, don't just stand there. Better go and line up back-stage.
Rowena I was just having a little tremble in the wash-room. I've got those butterflies back in my stomach again. Wish me luck, somebody!
Jennings I will. Jolly good luck, Rowena. I'll be keeping my fingers crossed for you.
Rowena (*astounded*) *You* will? Honestly?
Jennings All of us. We're all on your side. You know that.
Rowena How *could* I know it? All the things you've said! All the things you've done to stop me practising!
Jennings Only fooling, Rowena! We're all in this together, aren't we!
Rowena Gosh, that's marvellous. I feel better all ready.

MUSIC 21. *UNMUSICAL MOB* (reprise)

I've been so apprehensive and so melancholy
Trembling like a jelly on a dinner-trolley.
If you mean what you say
You've really made my day;
(*Speaking*) I'll go and show them there's a new star on the musical horizon.
(*Singing*) One day I'm going to be famous,
Get my own back on them all,

Prove that I'm no ignoramus
When I play at the Festival Hall.
Play at the Festival—
I'll be the best of all—
Play at the Festival Hall.

Distant applause is heard from the dining-hall

Jennings Go on, then. That's your cue. You're on now.
Rowena No need to panic! No need to hurry! I'm going to make a theatrical entrance.

Rowena starts to make a dignified exit, but collides in the doorway with Emma, Venables, Darbishire and Temple entering hurriedly from the dining-hall. Rowena struggles past them and exits

Emma Hey, come on Jennings. Aren't you ready? We're on after Rowena.
Darbishire Where's Mr Wilkins? He should be here by now.
Jennings He's not going to be in it. He's refused to go on.

Reaction

Darbishire Oh gosh, no!
Emma This is terrible. Whatever are we going to do?
Jennings Don't get in a flap. I've fixed everything up with the proper Henry the Fifth. He's going to take his place.
Venables You're off your runners! He's been dead about five hundred years.
Jennings Don't worry. You chaps are in for a surprise.
Temple So will the audience be when Henry the Fifth doesn't come on.
Jennings Got your trumpet, Emma? Everybody ready?
Emma How can we be ready if we haven't got the leading man!
Jennings Oh go *on*! Do as I tell you. It's going to be all right. At least I hope it is.
Emma I'm not taking the blame if everyone boos and hisses.

Emma and the others exit to the dining-hall, chivvied out by Jennings, who follows. Matron enters along the landing, followed by Borrowmore in chain mail and helmet and carrying a sword

Matron goes to the dining-hall door, opens it, and listens for a moment. Rowena's piano solo, "The Merry Peasant" (recorded) is heard. The music is cut off as Matron closes the door

Matron It's all right. There's a piano solo first. You're in good time.
Borrowmore Good. Never been late for an entrance in my life.
Matron It's so kind of you to help them out. They don't know how lucky they are having a famous professional actor to play their scene with them.
Borrowmore Famous professional actor. Ha! Are you joking! "Don't ring us, we'll ring you."
Matron I beg your pardon?

Borrowmore That's all right, I'm used to it. One has one's ups and downs, of course, but let's face it: fifty years on the stage and I'm still only on the fringe of the profession.

MUSIC 22.   *NO ROOM IN THE PROFESSION*

Borrowmore 1. Some people seek their livelihood in very dubious ways
   By methods that do not appeal to me   .
   Like taming lions or jumping out of planes by parachute
   Or pumping oil from under the North Sea
   But there's a job which to my mind is infinitely worse
   A form of self-inflicted punishment.
   You smear your face with greasepaint: you stand upon
      a stage
   And hope you'll make enough to pay the rent.

   2. Rum, tiddly tee
   Don't talk that way to me
   An actor's life is precarious
   He earns his living by various
   Means, which are most nefarious
   When he can't get on T.V.

   3. Don't be misled by the glamour
   Don't be dazzled by the lights
   Don't let them pull
   The wool
   Over your eyes
   It's no surprise
   That there isn't any room in the profession
   To stick your elbows out, or so it seems
   Yet in spite of our misgivings
   We still try to earn our livings
   In this overcrowded, over-rated
   Never ending, round-the-bending
   World of vanished dreams.

   4. It's no good having talent if you haven't got the luck
   A fact which some of us are slow to face.
   For after years of trailing at the heels of Goddess Drama
   I'm running hard to stay in the same place.
   I hoped, when I was young, they'd ask me to play Romeo.
   Now, they say, I'm too old for King Lear
   So thank God for Krunchie-Wunchie Cat Food adverts
   on T.V.
   It pays the rent and buys my pint of beer.

   5. (repeat of Verse 2)
   Rum, tiddly tee

Don't talk that way to me
An actor's life is precarious
He earns his living by various
Means, which are most nefarious
When he can't get on T.V.

6. (repeat of Verse 3)
Don't be misled by the glamour
Don't be dazzled by the lights
Don't let them pull
The wool
Over your eyes
It's no surprise
That there isn't any room in the profession
To stick your elbows out, or so it seems
Yet in spite of our misgivings
We still try to earn our livings
In this overcrowded, over-rated
Never ending, round-the-bending
World of vanished dreams.

Mr Carter enters from the dining-hall

*As the door opens Emma blows a fanfare and "Henry V" dialogue is heard
distantly*

Venables (*off*) "Where is the King?"
Jennings (*off*) "The King himself is rode to view the battle."
Temple (*off*) "Of fighting men they have full threescore thousand."

The door swings shut. The off stage dialogue fades

Mr Carter I'm glad you've changed your mind then, Wilkins. The boys
were relying on you to . . .

Borrowmore turns towards Carter

Oh, I beg your pardon. I thought you were—er—what's going on?
Borrowmore Understudy.
Mr Carter I see. Just as well really. I can't see that Wilkins would have
been much use after his first three lines. In fact, I . . .
Borrowmore Quiet, please, I'm waiting for my cue. Open the door, will
you.

Mr Carter opens the dining-hall door. "Henry V" dialogue is heard

Darbishire (*off*) "Then joyfully—my noble Lord of Bedford,
         My dear Lord Gloucester, and my good Lord Exeter,
         And my kind kinsmen, warriors all, adieu!"
Jennings (*off*) "Farewell, good Salisbury; and good luck go with thee!"
Temple (*off*) "Farewell, kind Lord. Fight valiantly today:
         And yet I do thee wrong to mind thee of it,
         For thou art fram'd of the firm truth of valour."

Jennings (*off*) "He is as full of valour as of kindness; Princely in both."

Emma enters from the dining-hall, panic-stricken and holding the prompt book. She rushes to Mr Carter

The "Henry V" dialogue continues

Emma ⎫	Sir! Sir! What shall we do! We haven't got a . . . ⎫	
	(*She sees Mr Borrowmore and gasps in disbelief*)	
Venables ⎬	(*off*) "Oh that we now had here	⎬ *Speaking*
	But one ten thousand of those men in	*together*
	England	
⎭	That do no work today." ⎭	

Borrowmore (*calling through the door*) "What's he that wishes so? My cousin Westmoreland? No, my fair cousin:

Borrowmore exits to the dining-hall, brandishing his sword

(*off*) "If we are mark'd to die, we are enow
      To do our country loss—"
Emma Who's he then? Where did he spring from?
Borrowmore (*off*) "—and if to live,
      The fewer men, the greater share of honour.
      God's will! I pray thee wish not one man more."

Emma shrugs and exits to the dining-hall, closing the door

Borrowmore (*off*) "By Jove, I am not covetous for gold,
      Nor care I who doth feed upon my cost . . ."

The "Henry V" dialogue becomes inaudible

MUSIC 23. *IT'S NOT EASY TO FORGET*

Mr Carter (*turning towards Matron and laughing*) Don't you wish you were in it, too?
Matron I do, rather. It's a wonderful age to be—

1. Children on the stage—take me back in memory
   Recall in a thousand ways
   All those dreams I dreamed, all those crazy plans I planned
   Back in my girlhood days.

2. I remember well, living out my fantasies
   Role-playing in my mind
   Acting out my hopes, dramatizing all my fears
   In those days that I've left behind.

3. I'd be Juliet or Ophelia, Desdemona or Cordelia—
   Or Rosalind according to my mood
   It drove my
   Boy friends to distraction: all this histrionic action
   Wasn't me—but just a mask.

I remember still all the things I used to do
It's not easy to forget that we were young like them.

Carter 4. Once upon a time, I used to think the whole wide world
Would be at my feet one day
All the triumphs I'd win, all the noble deeds I'd do
Slowly they've faded away.

5. I remember when, just like any other boy
I dreamed my dream of fame
I'd bestride the earth, scale the highest mountain top
Life was no more than a game.

6. I was Superman, an astronaut, a champion at every sport
A Derby winner on a donkey on the sands
O—lym—pic
Medals on my chest proved I was easily the best
In my imagination.
I remember still all the things I used to do
It's not easy to forget that we were young like them.

Matron 7. But did you never slay a dragon?
Carter   No, not ever.
Matron   Ride a horse in shining armour?
Carter   Well, not really
Matron   Rescue a fair damsel in distress?
Carter   Not yet, but—just—give me the chance!

Both   I remember still, all the things I used to do
It's not easy to forget that we were young like them.

Applause is heard off, as the concert finishes

*The Headmaster, Mr Wilkins, Borrowmore and all the Children enter
from the dining-hall, some carrying musical instruments, with excited
general conversation. Mr Wilkins exits through the archway to the staff
room and returns with the alarm clock*

Mr Wilkins (*moving to Jennings*) I gather from Mr Carter, Jennings, that
there was some misunderstanding about that little episode in class
yesterday, so I've decided to let you have this back. (*He hands the clock
to Jennings*)
Jennings Oh, thank you, sir. Thank you very much indeed. It's just what
we need, isn't it Darbi.
Darbishire Better wrap it up though. It is a present, after all.
Jennings Yes, of course. (*He removes his corrugated cardboard breastplate
and wraps it round the clock*) Matron, as it's your birthday and because
you're so decent I want to give you this present on behalf of everybody.

Reaction from everyone: "Good old Matron"

Matron (*taking the clock*) Oh, how lovely. How very kind of you. But you shouldn't have spent your money on me, you know.

Jennings We didn't, Matron—or rather, we didn't *mean* to—or rather, we hope it's what you want.

Matron It's just the thing. I've got to get up specially early tomorrow to call Mr Wilkins for his early train. How do I set it for six o'clock?

Jennings helps her to set the hands

Jennings I'll show you . . . There! It won't go off till six o'clock tomorrow.

Darbishire goes to Jennings and speaks in a loud whisper

Darbishire Hey, Jennings! What about my famous speech? I took a lot of trouble preparing it.

Jennings Gosh, yes. I'd forgotten about you and your speech.

Darbishire It's really in honour of Sir, but it'd go down just as well if I changed the names round.

Jennings Okay, you'd better do it now and get it over with. (*Loudly*) Attention, please! I now call upon C. E. J. Darbishire to address the gathering with a few well-chosen words.

Reaction: "Good old Darbi!"

Darbishire H'm. Matron and Guests. Unaccustomed as I am to public speaking, it gives me much pleasure to be very happy to—er—very happy to—er— . . . (*In sudden panic*) Oh fish-hooks, I've forgotten what comes next. Happy *something*—happy—happy . . .

Jennings (*singing*) Happy Birthday to you,
                 Happy Birthday to you,
All (*singing*)   Happy Birthday, dear Matron,
                 Happy Birthday to you!

The alarm clock suddenly shrills out. Matron, startled, drops the clock which is caught by Mr Carter standing beside her. Laughter and cheering from the Children. The Headmaster signals for silence

Headmaster Well now: this has been a most successful concert which we've all enjoyed very much.

Mr Wilkins Hear, hear.

Headmaster We must remember the people who have worked hard to entertain us—Matron for making these splendid costumes; Jennings and his heavily armoured barons; and, of course, Mr Irving Borrowmore for acting on King Henry the Fifth's inspired orders and stepping into the breach with seconds to spare. Nor must we forget to thank Mr Wilkins who so modestly stepped out of the breach so that Mr Borrowmore could step *into* it.

Cheers and applause

Well, it's all over now. All that remains is for us to mark the close of another term in our traditional way by singing our school song. But before we do so, let us give three hearty cheers: one for the term's hard work, one for the concert that brings it to an end, and, last and loudest, one for the holidays. Hip, hip—

Cheers

MUSIC 24. *SCHOOL SONG*

The cast sing the fourth and fifth verses only, as—

the CURTAIN *falls*

FINALE

The CURTAIN *rises on an empty stage. The various groups enter, singing*

MUSIC 25. *CROSSING OFF THE DAYS* (reprise)

All the extra Children enter singing the chorus only. They join in all the songs as the others enter

MUSIC 26. *RHUBARB* (reprise)

Jennings, Darbishire, Venables and Temple enter singing verses six and eight

MUSIC 27. *MATRON'S BIRTHDAY* (reprise)

Emma, Chris and Rowena enter singing the last verse

MUSIC 28. *FIRE DRILL* (reprise)

Mr Carter, Mr Wilkins, the Headmaster, Matron and Borrowmore enter singing the last verse

MUSIC 29. *SCHOOL SONG* (reprise)

The Company sing verses one, two, three and five—or verse five only

CURTAIN

FURNITURE AND PROPERTY LIST

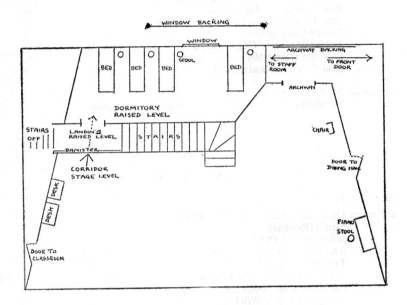

ACT I

On stage: Piano and stool
Electric bell and bell-push
Notice board
Display of challenge cups
2 pupils' desks and chairs
4 beds with bedding and red blankets
4 stools
4 dressing-gowns, pyjamas, slippers
Pair of shoes under **Jennings'** bed
Linen bag
Textbook (*Macbeth*) in pupil's desk
Playing-card with adhesive on piano

Off stage: Stack of exercise books **(Mr Wilkins)**
Pile of linen **(Matron)**
Notice for board **(Headmaster)**
Guinea pig cage, musical instruments, table-tennis bats, boxing gloves,
glove puppets, chess set glued to board, etc. **(Extra Children)**

Cocoa tin earphones, with string **(Jennings)**
Snorkel—4 ft. hose and funnels **(Emma, Chris)**
Crash helmet **(Darbishire)**
Cardboard telescope **(Darbishire)**
Green netting vegetable bags **(Emma, Chris, Girls)**
Plastic goldfish-bowl **(Emma)**
String hammock **(Extra Girls)**
Music—"Merry Peasant" **(Rowena)**
Bundle of letters **(Mr Carter)**
Parcel containing cake tin **(Mr Carter)**
Towels **(Matron)**
Folder of reports **(Mr Wilkins)**
Cake tin **(Darbishire)**
Roll Call list **(Headmaster)**

Personal: **Mr Carter:** watch, list of concert items
       Darbishire: false moustache with adhesive, spectacles

ACT II

SCENE 1

Set: Dormitory beds remade
Off stage: Desks and chairs **(Form 3 Children)**
      Music **(Rowena)**
      Suitcases **(All Children)**
      6 textbooks of *Henry V* **(Emma)**
      Trumpet **(Emma)**
      Alarm clock in box **(Jennings)**
      Pile of exercise books **(Mr Carter)**
      Poetry book **(Mr Wilkins)**
      Poetry books **(Form 3 Children)**
      File of reports **(Headmaster)**

Personal: **Extra Boy:** watch

SCENE 2

Strike: Desks and chairs
Off stage: Music **(Rowena)**
      Henry V textbook **(Emma)**
      9 envelopes with birthday cards **(Mr Carter)**
      4 swords, helmets, cloaks **(Chris)**
      4 *Henry V* costumes **(Matron)**
      1 small tunic **(Matron)**
      1 cardboard breastplate **(Matron)**
      1 pair plastic leg guards **(Matron)**
      File of reports **(Mr Wilkins)**
      Coal-scuttle **(Jennings)**

Suitcase containing armour **(Borrowmore)**
Trumpet **(Emma)**
Alarm clock **(Mr Wilkins)**
Helmet, sword **(Borrowmore)**

Personal: **Borrowmore:** chain mail (worn under day clothes to facilitate quick
change)

LIGHTING PLOT

Property fittings required: pendant in dormitory. N.B. Pendants in hall are inadvisable as they would mask the raised dormitory: wall brackets are optional, or lights may be imagined high in the ceiling
A hall and dormitory. The same scene throughout

ACT I Evening
To open: Full artificial light in hall. Dormitory lighting out

Cue 1	**Matron** enters dormitory *Bring up dormitory lighting*	(Page 2)
Cue 2	**Matron** leaves dormitory *Take out dormitory lighting*	(Page 2)
Cue 3	**Girls** enter in space headgear *Cross-fade hall lighting and special effect "space" lighting*	(Page 6)
Cue 4	**Boys** enter at end of EARTHMAN, GO HOME! song *Cross-fade to normal hall lighting*	(Page 8)
Cue 5	Song—THE THINGS THEY DO *Fade to spots on* **Wilkins, Matron, Carter**	(Page 15)
Cue 6	At end of song *Return to normal hall lighting*	(Page 16)
Cue 7	**Matron** switches on dormitory lights *Snap on dormitory lighting*	(Page 21)
Cue 8	**Darbishire** enters dormitory *Take out hall lighting*	(Page 22)
Cue 9	**Mr Wilkins** descends stairs. Voices of **Masters** off *Bring up hall lighting*	(Page 23)
Cue 10	**Headmaster, Wilkins, Carter** exit *Take out hall lighting*	(Page 25)
Cue 11	**Matron** switches off dormitory light *Snap off main dormitory lighting, leaving light from window and landing*	(Page 27)
Cue 12	**Jennings** starts to descend stairs. Voices of **Masters** off *Bring up hall lighting*	(Page 28)
Cue 13	**Mr Wilkins** rings bell *Snap on dormitory lighting*	(Page 30)

ACT II, Scene 1 Afternoon
To open: Full general lighting in hall—daylight

EFFECTS PLOT

ACT I

Cue 1	On CURTAIN up	**(Page 1)**
	School Song—recorded—verses 4 and 5	
Cue 2	At end of School Song—**Carter** rings bell	**(Page 2)**
	Electric bell	
Cue 3	**Carter** rings bell	**(Page 21)**
	Electric bell	
Cue 4	**Matron** opens window	**(Page 27)**
	Faint thud of falling cake tin	
Cue 5	**Wilkins**: ". . . anyone still in here when I get back."	**(Page 30)**
	Electric bell as **Wilkins** *rings it*	
Cue 6	**Jennings** exits through archway	**(Page 30)**
	Front door slams	

ACT II

SCENE 1

Cue 7	**Jennings**: ". . . got a fabulous bell. Listen!"	**(Page 42)**
	Alarm clock bell	
Cue 8	**Temple**: ". . . rhubarb, rhubarb, rhubarb."	**(Page 43)**
	Electric bell rings as extra **Boy** *rings it*	
Cue 9	**Wilkins**: "Ring out wild bells . . ."	**(Page 45)**
	Alarm clock bell	
Cue 10	Class in uproar	**(Page 46)**
	Alarm clock bell	

SCENE 2

Cue 11	**Carter** rings bell	**(Page 51)**
	Electric bell	
Cue 12	**Wilkins**: "my last word." (He opens door)	**(Page 53)**
	School Song while door is open	
Cue 13	**Rowena** opens door	**(Page 55)**
	School Song while door is open	

Cue 14   End of UNMUSICAL MOB reprise   (Page 56)
Distant applause—bring up as **Emma** *and others enter—fade as* **Rowena** *shuts door*

Cue 15   **Matron** opens door   (Page 56)
"Merry Peasant" piano solo. Fade as door shuts

Cue 16   Concert finishes   (Page 60)
Applause, off

Cue 17   End of HAPPY BIRTHDAY TO YOU   (Page 61)
Alarm clock bell

MADE AND PRINTED IN GREAT BRITAIN BY
LATIMER TREND & COMPANY LTD PLYMOUTH
MADE IN ENGLAND